ITALIAN BRONZE STATUETTES

AN EXHIBITION ORGANIZED BY
THE ARTS COUNCIL OF GREAT BRITAIN WITH
THE ITALIAN MINISTRY OF EDUCATION AND
THE RIJKSMUSEUM, AMSTERDAM

THE VICTORIA AND ALBERT MUSEUM, LONDON

27TH JULY TO 1ST OCTOBER 1961

THE ARTS COUNCIL 1961

FOREWORD

The proposal to hold an exhibition of Italian bronze statuettes originated with the Direzione Generale delle Antichità e Belle Arti, Ministero della Pubblica Istruzione, Rome, in 1958. Subsequently, at the suggestion of Dr A. F. E. van Schendel, Director-General of the Rijksmuseum, Amsterdam, it was proposed that the exhibition should be organized by the Ministry jointly with the Rijksmuseum and the Arts Council of Great Britain. The Arts Council, having been assured of the full support of the Victoria and Albert Museum from its Director, Sir Trenchard Cox, and from Mr John Pope-Hennessy, Keeper of the Department of Sculpture, warmly agreed. The Council has also been deeply indebted to the keen interest and encouragement of His Excellency Signor Vittorio Zoppi, Italian Ambassador in London and of his successor, His Excellency Signor Pietro Quaroni.

The successful conclusion of this international co-operation has resulted in the first full-scale exhibition of this art to be held in any country, and it should provide a valuable opportunity for the further study and reappraisal of the whole subject. Except for a small number of scholars and collectors, the informed taste of the last fifty years has neglected, as unsympathetic, the classic art of the small bronzes of the fifteenth to the seventeenth centuries, while concentrating its attention and enthusiasm on expressionist and romantic schools of sculpture and on the comparatively recently discovered art of primitive cultures. We hope that many visitors to this exhibition will realize for the first time the enjoyment which can be obtained from these works.

The Council wishes to record with gratitude its happy collaboration with Dr Bruno Molajoli, the recently appointed Director-General of the Direzione Generale delle Antichità e Belle Arti; Dr Gino Bacchetti, Inspector at the Ministero della Pubblica Istruzione; Dr Guglielmo Triches of the Direzione Generale delle Antichità e Belle Arti; Professor Emilio Lavagnino, Soprintendente alle Gallerie de Lazio, Rome, and *commissario* for the exhibition in Italy; Dr A. F. E. van Schendel and Mr T. H. Lunsingh Scheurleer, Keeper of the Department of Sculpture and Applied Arts, of the Rijksmuseum, in the preparation of the exhibition. It has also received valuable help from Professor Gabriele Baldini, Director of the Italian Institute, London; Monsieur Cyrille Arnavon, Cultural Counsellor, and Miss Renée Cameron of the French Embassy, London, and also Mr John Graham of the British Council office, Rome.

The original conception of the exhibition was ably planned by Professor Dr Antonino Santangelo, Director of the Museo di Palazzo Venezia, Rome, who has selected the works from Italian collections. To these some additional pieces were added at the request of

Mr Pope-Hennessy. Dr Santangelo has also been responsible for the compilation of the entries in the catalogue relating to works from public and private collections in Italy.

To Mr Pope-Hennessy the Council owes a very special debt of thanks, for without his enthusiasm, deep knowledge of the subject and untiring activity it would be true to say that this exhibition could hardly have been realized in this country. He was responsible for the selection of the works coming from outside Italy. He has also planned the arrangement and presentation of the exhibition, which poses perhaps more than any other type of exhibition great problems of display. To show effectively small objects, an essentially intimate art, under museum conditions, calls for taste and ingenuity of a special degree.

Lastly, we wish to thank most warmly all those who have made the exhibition possible, both those responsible for public collections and the private collectors throughout five European countries who have so generously contributed loans to the exhibition. Their names are given elsewhere in this catalogue, but we should like to record our special gratitude to Her Majesty The Queen, who has graciously lent four reliefs by Soldani from the Royal Collection; Professor Filippo Rossi, Soprintendente alle Gallerie per le provincie di Firenze, Arezzo e Pistoia and Director of the Museo Nazionale, Florence; Professor Cesare Gnudi, Soprintendente alle Gallerie per le provincie di Bologna, Ferrara, Forli, e Ravenna; Dottoressa Augusta Quintavalle, Soprintendente alle Gallerie per le provincie di Modena e Reggio Emilia; Professor Giuseppe Marchini, Soprintendente alle Gallerie per le Marche; Dr Oreste Ferrari, of the Museo Nazionale di Capodimonte, Naples; Dr Italo Faldi, Director of the Galleria Doria; Dr Rosanna Pincelli, of the Museo Civico, Bologna; Dr Gaetano Panazza and Dr Alessandro Peroni, of the Musei Civici, Brescia; Professor Vittorio Moschini, Soprintendente alle Gallerie del Veneto; Dr Giovanni Mariacher and Dr Terisio Pignatti, of the Museo Correr, Venice; Dr Alessandro Prosdocimi of the Museo Civico, Padua; Dr J. C. Ebbinge Wubben, Director of the Museum Boymans-van Beuningen, Rotterdam; the Victoria and Albert Museum, which has lent no less than 30 works; Sir Karl Parker, Keeper, and the Visitors of the Ashmolean Museum, Oxford, to whom we are so often deeply indebted for loans; and lastly, Monsieur Pierre Verlet, Keeper of the Department of Objets d'Art, and Monsieur Hubert Landais, Musée du Louvre, and Dr Hermann Fillitz, Kunstkammer Leiter, Kunsthistorisches Museum, Vienna, for generously making available a number of key pieces of types not available in Italian, English or Dutch collections, without which the exhibition would not have been fully representative.

The exhibition will be shown subsequently at the Rijksmuseum from October 28 to January 14, and then in Florence in the early part of 1962.

GABRIEL WHITE

INTRODUCTION

The period we know as the Renaissance is so called because it witnessed a conscious return to the antique. In the fifteenth century many Roman small bronzes were known, and the bronze statuette in the Renaissance originated in an effort to revive this classical art form. As in other departments of art, so in the small bronze, the works that resulted were utterly unclassical, but in the fifteenth and sixteenth centuries most of the works included in this exhibition would have been shown beside antiques. They were made for private individuals, often for practical use, and were intended to be handled, not seen formally in cases behind glass. So intimate are they that the very conception of an exhibition of bronze statuettes is in one sense a betrayal of their inner character. It is justified by the fact, first that they include a large number of great works of art, and second that they carry us into the very centre of Renaissance life.

For Renaissance sculptors bronze was as a medium second only in significance to marble, and the Renaissance in the visual arts is generally dated from the commissioning of a work in bronze, the first of the two doors cast by GHIBERTI (1378–1455) for the Baptistry in Florence. So far as can be ascertained, Ghiberti made no independent statuettes, but two small gilt bronze figures of Saints at Città di Castello have been ascribed to him (No. 2).

The history of the bronze statuette starts with DONATELLO (1386–1466), who made three famous figures of Putti for the font in the Baptistry in Siena. A number of bronzes by or from the circle of Donatello are shown in the exhibition. Bronze sculpture in the later fifteenth century stems directly from Donatello, and was developed with most energy in the three centres in which he worked, Siena (where he was employed from 1457 till 1461 on bronze doors for the cathedral), Florence (where he produced such works as the bronze *David* in the Bargello and the *Judith* in the Piazza della Signoria), and Padua (where he executed bronze sculptures for the high altar of Sant'Antonio).

Sienese bronze sculpture is represented in the exhibition by the eloquent relief of the *Flagellation* by FRANCESCO DI GIORGIO (1439–1501/2) from the Galleria Nazionale at Perugia (No. 23), and by a small group of related works. In Florence, Donatello's most notable successors were ANTONIO POLLAJUOLO (*c.* 1432–1498), VERROCCHIO (1435–1488) and BERTOLDO (*c.* 1420–1491). Pollajuolo's most famous bronze is the group of *Hercules and Antaeus* (No. 8) in the Bargello, Florence, which in the late fifteenth century was in the Medici collection. No small bronzes by Verrocchio are known, but he was responsible for one splendid work of applied art, the documented candlestick of 1468 made for the

Palazzo Vecchio in Florence, now in the Rijksmuseum, Amsterdam (No. 10). As a maker of small bronzes Bertoldo is a more substantial figure, by virtue of a bronze battle relief after the antique in the Bargello, which was made for Lorenzo de' Medici and is described by Vasari (No. 14). Other masterpieces by Bertoldo are the *Hercules on Horseback* from the Museo Estense at Modena (No. 15) and the poetic bronze of *Orpheus* or *Arion* from the Museo Nazionale, Florence (No. 13).

The most important bronze caster of the generation after that of Verrocchio and Bertoldo was Verrocchio's pupil, GIOVANNI FRANCESCO RUSTICI, best known for the great bronze group of the *Preaching of the Baptist* over the north door of the Baptistry in Florence, in the planning of which he was advised by Leonardo. Vasari describes a bronze *Mercury* which was commissioned from Rustici for a fountain at the Palazzo Medici by Cardinal Giulio de' Medici soon after the Medici returned to Florence, in 1515. This has been lent from a private collection (No. 21). Some of the most fascinating small bronzes of this time are a group of statuettes of horses, apparently cast from models made by LEONARDO DA VINCI for the fresco of the *Battle of Anghiari* (1505). One of these is shown (No. 20).

In Padua bronze casting was developed by Donatello's pupil BELLANO (c. 1435–before 1496/7 along naturalistic lines. Works in the exhibition by this deeply individual artist include the splendid *St Jerome* from the Louvre (No. 38), the *Europa and the Bull* from the Bargello (No. 41) and the *Mountain of Hell* from the Victoria and Albert Museum (No. 42). Bellano's naturalism was refined by his pupil Riccio, the supreme master of the bronze statuette. A mouthpiece of Paduan humanism, RICCIO (active after 1496; d. 1532) produced a quantity of classicizing bronzes and reliefs, many of them destined for practical use. Never before has so large a group of Riccio's works been brought together; these have been chosen to provide a picture not merely of his style, but of the imaginative world in which he moved. The works assembled include the relief of *St Martin and the Beggar* from the Ca d'Oro in Venice (No. 45), the *Shepherd with a Goat* (No. 56), the *Abundance* (No. 57) and a *Seated Satyr* (No. 58) from the Bargello, the *Demon* from Belluno (No. 52) and the *Pan* from the Ashmolean Museum (No. 49) (which many students would regard as the most beautiful small bronze in the world). Riccio's principal follower, DESIDERIO DA FIRENZE (active after 1532), is represented by his single documented work, the voting urn from the Museo Civico at Padua (No. 74).

The picture of Venetian bronze sculpture in the first quarter of the sixteenth century is still confused; key works here are the so-called Barbarigo altar, a relief from which is included in the exhibition (No. 91), and two signed reliefs by the associate of Giovanni Bellino, CAMELIO, one of which is also shown (No. 93). In an interesting group of anonymous Venetian bronzes, special interest attaches to the *St John the Baptist* ascribed to Antonio Lombardo from the Ashmolean Museum, Oxford (No. 88), and to the small busts of women by Tullio Lombardo from Modena (No. 89). From the same classical current come the romantic bronzes ascribed to FRANCESCO DA SANT'AGATA (active *c*, 1520), of which the most notable are the *Hercules* from Oxford (No. 83) and the *Faun playing a Double Flute* from the Louvre (No. 84).

In Mantua, under the inspiration of Mantegna, a large number of statuettes after the antique were produced for the Gonzaga court. The principal Mantuan bronze sculptor is ANTICO (d. 1528), whose name recently came into prominence through the purchase by the Victoria and Albert Museum of a parcel-gilt statuette of *Meleager* (No. 29). One of the most beautiful of Antico's parcel-gilt bronzes is the *Apollo Belvedere* in the Ca d'Oro, Venice (No. 28), which is shown with the *Hercules with a Club* from Vienna (No. 27). What is perhaps the finest surviving Mantuan relief in this style is the *Martelli Mirror*, in the Victoria and Albert Museum (No. 34).

In 1527 the great Florentine sculptor JACOPO SANSOVINO (1486–1570) arrived in Venice, bringing about a revolution in Venetian style. Of the many unsigned small bronzes ascribed to Sansovino two are universally accepted; these are the *Jupiter* in the Kunsthistorisches Museum at Vienna (No. 137) and the *Christ carrying the Cross* in the Museo Estense at Modena (No. 138). Both of these are exhibited. Sansovino's principal pupil DANESE CATTANEO (1509–1573) is represented by two well-known works, the *Luna* from Vienna (No. 140) and *Venus Marina* from the Museo Nazionale, Florence (No. 141). The most imposing Venetian bronze sculptor of the sixteenth century is, however, ALESSANDRO VITTORIA (1525–1608), here represented by a substantial group of works which include the *Winter* (No. 148) and *Negro Venus* (No. 150) from Vienna, the *Milo of Croton* from the Ca d'Oro in Venice (No. 149), and the *Neptune* from the Victoria and Albert Museum (No. 147).

The most prominent Venetian bronze sculptors of the close of the century, TIZIANO ASPETTI (1565–1607) and NICCOLO ROCCATAGLIATA (active 1593–1636), are also represented by blocks of works, those of the former headed by two unpublished bronzes lent by Mr Peter Harris (Nos. 163-4) and a figure of *Faith* from the Auriti collection, Rome (No. 165), and those of the latter by four music-making putti in gilt bronze from the collection of Mr Paul Wallraf (No. 171). The Venetian High Renaissance bronzes include two life-size busts by Vittoria (from the Ateneo Veneto) and by Danese Cattaneo (from the Museo Civico, Bassano) (Nos. 146 and 139 respectively).

The High Renaissance bronzes produced in Florence before the advent of Giovanni Bologna form a less familiar field. In some respects the most impressive bronze sculptor of the first half of the century is TRIBOLO (1500–1550). A bronze of Samson and two Philistines (Nos. 102-3), ascribed to PIERINO DA VINCI (1521–1544), depends from a lost model by Michelangelo. The exhibition also contains two bronzes by his less gifted contemporary BACCIO BANDINELLI (1493–1560) (Nos. 105-6). The only bronze statuettes that can be confidently given to Bandinelli's opponent, Benvenuto Cellini (1500–1570), are those on the base of the Perseus in the Loggia dei Lanzi in Florence, but from 1570 there dates the important commission for eight mythological bronze figures (on a scale midway between the statue and statuette) for the Studiolo of Francesco I de' Medici in the Palazzo Vecchio.

Some of the artists responsible for these figures certainly made small bronzes—examples by VINCENZO DANTI and AMMANATI are, for instance, included in the exhibition—and one, the Fleming GIOVANNI BOLOGNA (1529–1608), became the uncontested master of the sixteenth-century Florentine bronze statuette.

Perhaps his best-known figure is the *Mercury*, a model for which from Bologna (No. 120) is included in the exhibition. A still more imposing work of the same relatively early date is the large bronze model for the central figure of the *Fountain of Neptune* at Bologna (No. 116). Other works by Giovanni Bologna comprise two of the bronze putti from the Grimaldi Chapel at Genoa (No. 119), and the *Dwarf Morgante mounted on a Dragon* from the Bargello in Florence (No. 118) which originally formed part of a small fountain on the roof of the Loggia dei Lanzi.

The vehicle through which Giovanni Bologna's style was diffused was the bronze statuette, and his most popular models—such as the *Architecture* (No. 124) and the *Hercules and the Boar* (No. 122)—had an incalculable influence on European taste.

The bronze statuette in the seventeenth century has been less fully studied than that in the sixteenth. In Florence the scene is dominated by two pupils of Giovanni Bologna, ANTONIO SUSINI (d. 1624) and PIETRO TACCA (d. 1640), and by GIOVANNI FRANCESCO SUSINI (d. 1646). Both the Susini specialized in making bronzes after the antique; a typical signed example of these is Giovanni Francesco Susini's evocative adaptation of the Ludovisi *Ares* in the Museo delle Terme in Rome (No. 133). Pietro Tacca was a more adventurous, though in some respects a less sensitive, artist, one of whose pupils, FRANCESCO FANELLI worked in England for King Charles I. Two bronzes by Tacca (Nos. 134A and B) and two bronzes by Fanelli (Nos. 135 and 136) appear in the exhibition. The extreme end of the seventeenth century was marked by the resurgence of bronze sculpture in Florence, at the hands of GIOVANNI BATTISTA FOGGINI and MASSIMILIANO SOLDANI. In Northern Europe there was widespread demand for works by these two sculptors. The two works by Foggini exhibited (Nos. 199 and 200) were presented by Cosimo III de' Medici, Grand-Duke of Tuscany, in 1714 to the French painter Rigaud, and the four reliefs of the Seasons by Massimiliano Soldani (Nos. 193-6), graciously lent by Her Majesty The Queen, were cast in 1715 for an English patron, Lord Burlington. A Venetian artist of the time whose works were especially admired by visitors to Italy is FRANCESCO BERTOS, one of whose infinitely ingenious groups is lent by Mr Paul Wallraf (No. 201).

In Rome in the seventeenth century style was dominated by BERNINI, who, like Michelangelo before him, preferred the medium of marble to that of bronze. Some of Bernini's few fully authenticated bronzes are four decorative masks (No. 187A-D), which have remained in the possession of his descendants. Bronze plays a more important part in the work of Bernini's contemporary rival, ALESSANDRO ALGARDI, who is represented as a portrait sculptor by the magnificent bronze and porphyry bust of Pope Innocent X from the Palazzo Doria in Rome (No. 188), and as a maker of small bronzes by the important group of *St. Michael overcoming Satan* (No. 189), which was cast for S. Michele in Bosco at Bologna.

In selecting the works shown in this exhibition an attempt has been made, first to offer a representative history of the bronze statuette, second to represent in a worthy way the great artists by whom bronze statuettes were made, and third to juxtapose signed, documented or otherwise authenticated works with works whose attribution is conjectural. It is intended to provide a basis for the study of Italian bronze sculpture, and at the same time to offer a conspectus of some of the most individual, inventive and eloquent small sculptures that have ever been produced.

BIBLIOGRAPHICAL ABBREVIATIONS

B.F.A.C.	London, Burlington Fine Arts Club: *Catalogue of a Collection of Sculpture and other Plastic Art of the Renaissance*, 1913
Bode, *Denkmäler*	Bode, *Denkmäler der Renaissance-Sculptur Toscanas*, Munich, 1892–1905
Bode, *I.B.S.*	Bode, assisted by Murray Marks, *The Italian Bronze Statuettes of the Renaissance*, 3 vols., London, 1908–12
Catalogo 1898	Supino, *Catalogo del R. Museo Nazionale di Firenze*, Rome, 1898
Fortnum	*A Descriptive Catalogue of the Bronzes of European Origin in the South Kensington Museum*, London, 1876
Hermann	Hermann, 'Pier Jacopo Alari Bonacolsi gennant Antico,' in *Jahrbuch der Kunsthistorischen Sammlungen des A. H. Kaiserhauses*, xxviii, 1910, pp. 202–88
Hill	Hill, *A Corpus of Italian Medals of the Renaissance before Cellini*, 2 vols., Oxford, 1930
J.B..K.	*Jahrbuch der Preuszischen Kunstsammlungen*
Molinier	Molinier, *Les Plaquettes*, 2 vols., Paris, 1886
Planiscig, *Bronzeplastiken*	Kunsthistorisches Museum in Wien: *Die Bronzeplastiken*, bearbeitet von L. Planiscig, Vienna, 1924
Planiscig, *P.B.I.*	Planiscig, *Piccoli Bronzi Italiani del Rinasimento*, Milan, 1930
Planiscig, *V.B.*	Planiscig, *Venezianische Bildhauer der Renaissance*, Vienna, 1921
Pollak	*Raccolte Alfredo Barsanti*, Rome, 1922
Rizzini	*Illustrazione dei civici musei di Brescia*, Brescia, 1889
Santangelo	Museo di Palazzo Venezia, *Catalogo delle Sculture*, a cura di A. Santangelo, Rome, 1954
W.J.	*Jahrbuch der Kunsthistorischen Sammlungen des A.H. Kaiserhauses*, later *Jahrbuch der Kunsthistorischen Sammlungen in Wien*

THIRTEENTH CENTURY

TUSCANY

WORKSHOP OF NICOLA PISANO
(Active 1258–1278)

1 HEAD OF A WOMAN
h. 13 cm.
Fragment worked from a lump of ferrous ore from Elba. It may be regarded as a work of Nicola Pisano or one of his immediate followers executed in the years preceding the Fontana Maggiore in Perugia.
Coll: Formerly in the Museo Kircheriano.
Bibl: Santangelo, p. 17, pl. 4–5.
Museo di Palazzo Venezia, Rome

FIFTEENTH & EARLY SIXTEENTH CENTURIES

FLORENCE

LORENZO GHIBERTI
(b. Florence 1378–d. Florence 1455)

2 SAINTS ANDREW AND FRANCIS. Gilt bronze
h. 19·5 and 20·5 cm.
From the Church of S. Francesco, Città di Castello. Though these figures were seen by Certini (see below) flanking a silver reliquary of St Andrew of 1420, this cannot have been their original position. Considered by Schmarsow early works of Luca della Robbia, they are given by Venturi to Ghiberti, and by Middeldorf and Krautheimer to the workshop of this sculptor.
Bibl: Certini, *Origine delle Chiese e Monasteri di Città di Castello*, V, 1, 1726 (MS. Città di Castello, Archivio Capitolare); Magherini Graziani, *L'Arte a Città di Castello*, 1890, p. 308; Schmarsow, in *Festschrift zu Ehren des Kunsthistorischen Instituts in Florenz*, 1897, p. 68; Venturi, *Storia*, VI, p. 172; Fanfani, *Città di Castello*, 1927, pp. 48 f.; Middeldorf, in *Pantheon*, XVI, 1935, pp. 279 f.; Krautheimer, *Ghiberti*, 1956, pp. 119–20.
Pinacoteca, Città di Castello

DONATELLO
(b. Florence *c.* 1386–d. Florence 1466)

3 PUTTO   Plate 1
h. 38·5 cm.
Replica with variations of one of the music-making putti on the tabernacle of the Baptismal Font in the Baptistery at Siena. The putti were originally six in number; payment for three of them was made to Giovanni Turini on September 26, 1431, and three were executed by Donatello, presumably soon after April 16, 1428, when wax was purchased 'per fare le forme di cierti fanciulini inudi per lo Battesimo'. One of the Donatello putti had already been removed from the Font in the eighteenth century, and until the war was in the Kaiser Friedrich Museum, Berlin. Another putto by Donatello remains *in situ* on the Font. The attribution of the present putto to Donatello is rejected by Lanyi and Janson, both of whom ascribe it to a Sienese master of the late fifteenth century. Janson suggests that it was made for the font in substitution for a stolen figure by Giovanni Turini.

Bibl: Milanesi, *Documenti*, II, 135; Bode, *IBS*, I, pl. VI; Venturi, *Storia*, VI, p. 272; Planiscig, *PBI*, p. 4, pl. III (as Donatello); Lanyi, in *Burlington Magazine*, LXXV, 1939, 142–51; Janson, *The Sculpture of Donatello*, II, 1957, 74–5 (with exhaustive analysis).
Museo Nazionale, Florence

4 PUTTO WITH A DOLPHIN. Dark patination, with traces of gilding on the wings and dolphin
h. 40 cm.
Part of a wall fountain. At the back a circular aperture seems to have served for the introduction of a water pipe, and in front the water issued in two jets from the penis and from the mouth of the fish. On acquisition it was ascribed initially to the school of Verrocchio and later to the school or workshop of Donatello. A bronze statuette of a Putto with a Cornucopia in the Hermitage at Leningrad, with which the present figure is associated by Schottmüller, is by another hand. There are some affinities between the figure and the three winged putti on the capital beneath the external pulpit at Prato (which appears to have been modelled and worked up by Michelozzo), but the style supports a dating in the vicinity of the reliefs on the base of the Judith (*c.* 1455) rather than at any earlier time. It is likely that the figure was cast from a Donatello model, but was worked up by a studio hand.
Coll: Piot.
Bibl: Schottmüller, *Donatello*, 1904, p. 84 n(not entirely autograph); Bode, *IBS*, I, p. 10 ('can only be ascribed to his school'); Maclagan and Longhurst, 1932, p. 21 ('possibly rather a production of his workshop than of his hand').
Victoria and Albert Museum, London

STYLE OF DONATELLO

5 CHRIST ON THE CROSS WITH THE VIRGIN AND ST JOHN
h. 46 cm., w. 28·8 cm.
The relief, which was at one time generally ascribed to Donatello, is by an unknown pupil or imitator of this sculptor working in the third quarter of the fifteenth century. It is grouped by Janson with bronze reliefs of the Martyrdom of St Sebastian in the Musée Jacquemart-Andre, Paris, and of the Virgin and Child with two Angels holding Garlands in the Estensische Kunstsammlung, Vienna. The sculptor responsible for it seems to have been familiar with the bronze Crucifixion relief by Donatello in the Museo Nazionale, Florence, a work of *c.* 1455,

the authorship of which is wrongly contested by Janson.
Coll: Robinson, Camondo.
Bibl: Bode, *Denkmäler*, pl. 95A, p. 32 (as Donatello); Schubring, *Donatello*, 1907, p. 174; Janson, *The Sculpture of Donatello*, II, 1957, p. 244.
Musée du Louvre

6 ST JOHN THE BAPTIST
h. 56·2 cm.
At one time attributed to Michelozzo, the statuette derives from the late work of Donatello.
Bibl: Bode, *IBS*, p. 10, pl. IV (as school of Donatello); Venturi, *Storia*, VI, p. 363 (as ascribed to Michelozzo); Planiscig, *PBI*, pl. V, fig. 7 (as Florentine, second half of the fifteenth century).
Museo Nazionale, Florence

7 PUTTO WITH RIGHT ARM RAISED. Dark brown patination. Small casting flaw on right thigh
h. 16·5 cm.
The statuette, which appears to have formed part of some larger unit, is related to the work of Maso di Bartolommeo, but cannot be ascribed confidently to this hand.
Coll: Newall (presented to the Museum by the National Art-Collections Fund).
Bibl: *Review*, p. 1 (as 'probably by Donatello'); Planiscig, *PBI*, pl. XXXIV, fig. 36 (as Florentine, late fifteenth century).
Victoria and Albert Museum, London

ANTONIO DEL POLLAJUOLO
(b. Florence 1433–d. Rome 1498)

8 HERCULES AND ANTAEUS   Plate 6
Cire perdue cast, not chiselled
h. 44 cm.
In 1495 the bronze was listed in the Medici inventories as 'nella chamera che risponde sulla via chiamata di Monsignore, dove sta Giuliano'. Since it is a relatively early work by Pollajuolo, it was possibly executed on the commission of Lorenzo il Magnifico, and not on that of his son Giuliano de' Medici, duc de Nemours (d. 1516).
Bibl: Muntz, *Les collections des Medicis au XVe siècle*, p. 85; Catalogo, 1898, p. 385; Bode, *IBS*, I, pl. XV; Bode, *Denkmäler*, p. 138, pl. 434; Cruttwell, *Antonio del Pollajuolo*, 1907, pp. 81–2; Venturi, *Storia*, VI, p. 744; Planiscig, *PBI*, pl. XV; Sabatini, *Antonio e Piero del Pollajuolo*, 1944, p. 82; Ortolani, *Pollajuolo*, 1948, p. 215.
Museo Nazionale, Florence

9 DAVID
h. 33·7 cm.
Recognized as a work of Pollajuolo by Venturi in 1898.
Bibl: Filangieri di Candida, in *L'Arte*, I, 1898, pp. 188–9; Bode, *IBS*, pl. XV (as Antonio del Pollajuolo); Bode, *Denkmäler*, p. 139, pl. 5,490 (as Antonio del Pollajuolo); Planiscig, *PBI*, pl. XVIII (as Antonio del Pollajuolo); Sabatini, *Antonio e Piero del Pollajuolo*, 1944, p. 82 (as Antonio del Pollajuolo); Ortolani, *Il Pollajuolo*, 1948, p. 221 (as Antonio del Pollajuolo).
Museo Nazionale di Capodimonte, Naples

ANDREA DEL VERROCCHIO
(b. Florence 1435–d. Venice 1488)

10 CANDLESTICK. Dark brown patination
h. 157 cm.
On the base is an inscription MAGGIO E GIVGNO MCCCCLXVIII which enables the candlestick to be identified with a candlestick in the form of a vase ('a similitudine di certo vaso') commissioned from Verrocchio for the Sala dell'Udienza of the Palazzo della Signoria in Florence in 1468. Verrocchio received a sum of eight gulden for the candlestick on June 29, 1468, and a further forty gulden on September 23, 1469. The concluding payment was made on April 20, 1480, 'for the candlestick which stands in the Chapel of the Audience Chamber'. The significance of the date inscribed on the base is not clear; Valentiner suggests that it may refer to a bequest in connection with some event which took place during the early summer of 1468.
Coll: Chapel of the Reception Hall in the Palazzo Vecchio, Florence; Kunstkammer der Hohenzollern; Kaiser Friedrich Museum, Berlin; Mannheimer, Amsterdam; acquired by the Rijksmuseum 1952.
Exh: Decorative Arts of the Italian Renaissance, *1400–1600*, Detroit Institute of Arts, 1958–9, No. 231.
Bibl: Valentiner, in *Burlington Magazine*, LXII, 1933, pp. 328–32 (reprinted in *Studies of Italian Renaissance Sculpture*, 1950, pp. 98–101); Planiscig, *Andrea del Verrocchio*, 1941, pp. 15, 49, fig. 11.
Rijksmuseum, Amsterdam

FLORENTINE, c. 1475

11 CUPID WITH A BOW AND QUIVER. Dark brown patination. The figure let into a triangular base
h. 23·5 cm. (without base)
The bronze, which is unrecorded and exists in a single version, is evidently Florentine. Its style is generically Verrocchiesque, and it is not im-possible that it was made about 1470–1480 in the workshop of Verrocchio. The triangular base is of rather later date, and seems to have been produced in the first half of the sixteenth century.
Mrs Miriam Sacher, London

12 HEAD OF A CHILD
h. 20 cm.
The head may be compared with the work of Francesco di Simone Ferrucci and with derivatives from it by Tommaso Fiamberti and his companion Giovanni Ricci. There is no evidence, however, that any of these artists made bronze casts.
Bibl: Venturi, *Storia*, VI, p. 667; De Rinaldis, p. 371, No. 427.
Museo Nazionale di Capodimonte, Naples

BERTOLDO
(b. *c.* 1420–d. Poggio a Cajano 1491)

13 ARION. Cire perdue casting. The face and legs alone worked up   Plate 3
h. 44 cm.
From the Guardaroba of Lorenzo il Magnifico. It is wrongly suggested by Bode that a bronze shown in a portrait painted by Dorothea Therbusch in 1773 is a second version of the present statuette.
Bibl: Bode, *Denkmäler*, pl. 427C, pp. 134, 167; Bode, *IBS*, pl. X; Bode, *Bertoldo*, pp. 91–3; Venturi, *Storia*, VI, p. 514; Planiscig, *PBI*, p. xi.
Museo Nazionale, Florence

14 BATTLE RELIEF   Plate 2
43 × 99 cm.
Ideal reconstruction of the front of a much damaged Hadrianic sarcophagus formerly in the Abbey of S. Zeno and subsequently in the Camposanto at Pisa. The present relief is mentioned in the inventory of the effects of Lorenzo il Magnifico as 'nella saletta rimpetto alla sala grande' in the Palazzo Medici in Via Larga, Florence.
Bibl: Bode, *Denkmäler*, pl. 426B, pp. 133, 167; Bode, *Bertoldo*, pp. 53–60.
Museo Nazionale, Florence

15 HERCULES ON HORSEBACK   Plate 4
h. 27·5 cm.
Probably part of a decorative complex, perhaps on a piece of furniture, which also included the Hercules in the Liechtenstein collection in Vienna and its counterpart, which is known through a version in the Frick collection, New York. The representation symbolizes the house of Este, and particularly Ercole I (1471–1505).

Bibl: Bode, *IBS*, I, pl. XIII; Bode, *Bertoldo*, pp. 94–7; Planiscig, *PBI*, pl. VIII.
Museo Estense, Modena

16 HERCULES AND THE NEMEAN LION. Rich brown patination
h. 19 cm.
Perhaps made as the cover of an inkstand or other receptacle. Hill suggests, on the basis of a coin, that the bronze was made as one of a pair for Ercole d'Este; this is conjectural. The base is explained by Bode as a shield.
Bibl: Bode, *IBS*, I, p. 14, pl. XIV (as Bertoldo); Bode, *Bertoldo*, 1925, pp. 105–6 (as Bertoldo); Hill, in *Burlington Magazine*, XVI, 1910, p. 312 (as attributed to Bertoldo); *The Salting Bequest*, 1911 (as Bertoldo); Venturi, *Storia*, VI, 1908, p. 518 (as Bertoldo); Planiscig, *PBI*, p. 6, pl. XI, fig. 16 (as Bertoldo).
Victoria and Albert Museum, London

17 HERCULES WITH THE APPLES OF THE HESPERIDES. Dark patination. On a somewhat later triangular base
h. (without base) 33 cm.
Classified by Bode as a Florentine bronze after the antique, the model is not closely related to any antique prototype. If by Bertoldo, it represents the final phase of this sculptor's development.
Bibl: Hill, in *Burlington Magazine*, XIV, 1910, p. 312 (attributed to Bertoldo); Bode, *IBS*, II, p. 8, pl. CI (as reminiscent of Pollajuolo); Bode, *Catalogue of the Collection of Pictures and Bronzes in the Possession of Mr Otto Beit*, 1913, p. 59 (for second version in Beit collection).
Victoria and Albert Museum, London

18 THE EDUCATION OF CUPID. Dark patination. Casting flaws
h. 17·5 cm., w. 25 cm.
The relief shows (*right*) Vulcan forging a wing for Cupid, who is held up before him by a winged female figure (Venus?) and (*left*) Cupid standing before a seated figure of Mercury. A second version exists in Venice (Museo Correr). As noted by Bode, the relief was known to Carpaccio, who adapted it as a fictive marble relief in a scene of the St Ursula cycle. A cognate circular relief from the Bertoldo workshop is also known (version in Museum A.162-1910).
Coll: Pourtalès.
Bibl: Bode, *Denkmäler*, p. 135, pl. 430B (as Bertoldo); Bode, *Bertoldo*, 1925, pp. 80–1 (as Bertoldo); Planiscig, *Riccio*, 1927, pp. 41, 46 (as Bertoldo).
Victoria and Albert Museum, London

19 SEATED NUDE. The right foot and part of the leg are broken and missing
h. 22 cm.
Attributed to Bertoldo by Bode. It also reveals connections with the work of Adriano Fiorentino, who is known, from the signature on the Bellerophon in Vienna, to have cast works modelled by Bertoldo.
Bibl: De Rinaldis, p. 377, No. 429; Bode, *Bertoldo*, pp. 99–100.
Museo Nazionale di Capodimonte, Naples

LEONARDO DA VINCI
(b. Vinci 1452–d. France 1519)

20 REARING HORSE. Dark patination slightly rubbed
h. 23 cm.   Plate 8
The statuette forms one of a group of three horses by or after Leonardo, of which the most celebrated is a Riding Warrior at Budapest and the second is in the Metropolitan Museum of Art, New York. The horses are the only works of sculpture that can be directly associated with Leonardo, and certainly depend from models by this artist. It has been claimed that both the present bronze and that at Budapest are preparatory studies for Leonardo's Trivulzio monument, but, as noted by Clark, their closest affinities in Leonardo's work are with the drawings for the fresco of the Battle of Anghiari, and it is likely that they are casts from wax models for the fresco by Leonardo, and were made in Florence c. 1508.
Exh: Milan, 1939. R.A., 1952, No. 262.
Bibl: Jeannerat, in *Apollo*, XIX, 1934, pp. 312–16 (present bronze as study by Leonardo for the Trivulzio monument); Meller, in *PJ*, XXXVII, 1916, pp. 213–50 (Budapest bronze as study by Leonardo for the Trivulzio monument); Clark, *Leonardo da Vinci*, 1952, p. 144 (Budapest bronze as the work of 'a pupil who had before him one of Leonardo's smaller wax models'); Heydenreich, *Leonardo da Vinci*, 1954, p. 73 (Budapest bronze as after Leonardo's design); Brugnoli, in *Leonardo: saggi e ricerche*, 1955, p. 374.
Mr Pierre Jeannerat, London

GIOVANNI FRANCESCO RUSTICI
(b. Florence 1474–d. Tours 1554)

21 MERCURY. Brown patination. The mouth is bored to emit water; oval aperture in the back. On a stone ball
h. 46·2 cm.   Plate 9
The bronze is convincingly identified by Loeser as a fountain figure of Mercury said by Vasari to have been commissioned from Rustici for the Palazzo Medici by Cardinal Giulio de' Medici.

Vasari states that the Mercury was a naked figure standing on a ball, as though about to take off in flight and held in its extended hand a mechanical device with 'four delicate wings like those of a butterfly', which were rotated by water emitted from the mouth. The figure dates from 1515.

Coll: Wyndham Cook, Henry Harris.
Exh: Mostra Medicea, Palazzo Medici, Florence, 1939, Sala IX, No. 11.
Bibl: Loeser, in *Burlington Magazine*, LII, 1928, p. 266 (as Rustici); Venturi, *Storia*, X–i, 1935, p. 85n (as attributed to Rustici).
Private Collection

SIENA

VECCHIETTA
(b. Siena 1412–d. Siena 1480)

22 THE FLAGELLATION. Dark patination. In a contemporary walnut frame, partly gilded
h. (without frame) 23·5 cm., w. (without frame) 28·6 cm.
Purchased by Salting before 1904, when it was shown at the Burlington Fine Arts Club under an ascription to 'the manner of Francesco di Giorgio'. In the Museum (Salting Bequest) from 1910 as Sienese school. The relief is a characteristic work of Vecchietta of somewhat earlier date than the bronze Resurrection in the Frick collection, New York. There is no reason to doubt that the frame is that originally made for the relief.
Coll: Salting.
Bibl: The Salting Collection, 1911, p. 9 (as Sienese school); Weller, *Francesco di Giorgio*, 1943, p. 154 (tentative ascription to Giacomo Cozzarelli).
Victoria and Albert Museum, London

FRANCESCO DI GIORGIO MARTINI
(b. Siena 1439–d. Siena 1501)

23 THE FLAGELLATION   Plate 7
h. 56 cm., w. 41 cm.
Related in style and technique to the relief of the Lamentation over the Dead Christ in the Carmini in Venice, which was executed for the Oratorio della S. Croce in Urbino and is mentioned as being there by Lazzari, who also records its dedicatory inscription: Invictissimi Federici Urbini Ducis Oblatio (*Delle Chiese di Urbino*, Urbino, 1801, 86). Both reliefs may be dated at the beginning of Francesco di Giorgio's first stay in Urbino, about 1478.
Bibl: Venturi, in *L'Arte*, V, 1902, 43 (as Verrocchio), and VI, 1903, p. 508 (as Bertoldo); Bode, in *JB*, XXV, 1904, p. 125 (as Leonardo da Vinci); Fabriczy, in *Die Allgemeine Zeitung*, Beilage, February 15, 1906 (as Francesco di Simone); Schubring, *Die Plastik Sienas*, p. 186 (as Francesco di Giorgio); Hill, in *Burlington Magazine*, XVII, 1910, p. 143 (as Francesco di

Giorgio); Hartlaub, in *Pantheon*, XXV, 1940, p. 87 (as Francesco di Giorgio); Weller, *Francesco di Giorgio*, Chicago, 1943, p. 151 (as Francesco di Giorgio).
Galleria Nazionale dell'Umbria, Perugia

Attributed to FRANCESCO DI GIORGIO

24 ARION (?). Brown patination. Both arms broken
h. 25·5 cm.
The statuette is generally described (Planiscig and others) as a Bacchant; it is unlikely that this interpretation is correct. The skin with hooves recurs on a statuette of Orpheus or Arion by Bertoldo in the Museo Nazionale, Florence, and it is possible that the same subject is represented in the present figure, which may have been shown playing a lyre or other instrument. The claim (Weinberger) that the breaks in the two arms are deliberate, and that the figure is a forgery of an antique bronze, is unconvincing. Widely varying views have been expressed as to the authorship of the figure and its date. An attribution by Planiscig to Francesco di Giorgio has not won general acceptance, and the bronze, which certainly dates from the late fifteenth century, is possibly Florentine.
Bibl: Bode, *IBS*, p. 24, pl. CLXII (as Venetian, c. 1575); Schlosser, *Album ausgewählter Gegenstände der kunstindustriellen Sammlung des allerhöchsten Kaiserhauses*, 1901, p. 13, pl. XX/i (as Paduan or Venetian); Fabriczy, in *Repertorium für Kunstwissenschaft*, XXV, 1902, p. 225 (as Florentine, late fifteenth century); Planiscig, *Bronzeplastiken*, p. 6, No. 4 (as Florentine, last quarter of fifteenth century); Planiscig, in *WJ*, n.s., III, 1929, pp. 73–5 (as Francesco di Giorgio); Planiscig, *PBI*, pl. XXII, fig. 32 (as Francesco di Giorgio); Planiscig, in *Dedalo*, XII, 1932, p. 748 (as Francesco di Giorgio); Weinberger, in *Zeitschrift für Bildende Kunst*, LXV, 1931, pp. 53–4 (as 'Antikenfälschung', not by Francesco di Giorgio); Weller, *Francesco di Giorgio*, 1944, p. 336 (as not by Francesco di Giorgio).
Kunsthistorisches Museum, Vienna

CENTRAL ITALY

TUSCAN or EMILIAN (first half of fifteenth century)

25 SHIELD–BEARER
h. 24·8 cm.
The bronze shows a number of primitive characteristics, and in type is still redolent of the fourteenth century.
Coll: Palagi (No. 110).
Museo Civico, Bologna

CENTRAL ITALIAN (beginning of the sixteenth century)

26 SHE-WOLF WITH ROMULUS AND REMUS. Black patina
h. 11·5 cm.
Acquired by the Rijksmuseum in 1958.

After the antique bronze Wolf in the Palazzo dei Conservatori, Rome, to which figures of Romulus and Remus were added in the fifteenth century. Related bronzes deriving from the Capitoline Wolf are in the National Gallery of Art, Washington (Kress collection) (with both twins), the Kunsthistorisches Museum, Vienna (with one twin). In examples in the Frick collection, New York, and the former R. von Kauffmann collection, Berlin, the type of the wolf is markedly unlike that in the present bronze.
Bibl: The Frick Collection, V, 1953, pp. 3–4 (best analysis of model).
Rijksmuseum, Amsterdam

MANTUA

PIER JACOPO ALARI BONACOLSI called ANTICO
(b. *c.* 1460–d. Mantua 1528)

27 HERCULES WITH THE CLUB. Black lacquer and traces of brown natural patination. Index finger of left hand broken
h. 40·5 cm.
The figure originally held the apples of the Hesperides in the left hand. Identified by Schlosser with a 'Hercules del bastono' in the Mantua inventory of 1496 (Rossi, *Rivista Numismatica*, I, p. 167), it depends from an antique original of the type of a statue in the Palazzo Pitti. A weaker replica is in the Louvre.
Bibl: Bode, *IBS*, III, pl. CCXXXV; Schlosser, *Werke der Kleinplastik in der Skulturensammlung des A.H. Kaiserhauses*, I, 1910, p. 3, pl. VIII; Hermann, in *WJ*, XXVIII, 1910, p. 266; Planiscig, *Bronzeplastiken*, p. 55, No. 99; Planiscig, *PBI*, pl. CI, fig. 173.
Kunsthistorisches Museum, Vienna

28 APOLLO BELVEDERE. Parcel gilt. The eyes inlaid with silver
h. 40 cm.
Reduction from the Apollo Belvedere. To be identified with an 'Apollo simil a quello di Roma', which is listed in the inventory of Isabella d'Este, and with an Apollo made for Lodovico Gonzaga, the model for which was completed in 1498 and which was cast in bronze in 1501. After the death (1708) of Ferdinando Carlo Gonzaga,

the last Duke of Mantua, it was acquired by Domenico Pasqualigo, who later presented it to the Museo Archeologico del Palazzo Ducale in Venice.
Bibl: Hermann, in *WJ*, XXVIII, 1910, p. 201; Planiscig, *PBI*, pl. XCVIII.
Ca d'Oro, Venice

29 MELEAGER. Dark patination, parcel gilt (gilding on hair and cloak, sandals, beard and teeth), eyes inlaid with silver. Shaft of spear broken
h. 30·8 cm.   Plate 10
The bronze, which exists only in a single version, seems to derive from a sarcophagus relief, and the drapery at the back is therefore freer and less classical than that in front. Its facture is comparable to that of the Venus Felix in Vienna.
Bibl: National Art-Collections Fund, Fifty-seventh Annual Report, 1961, p. 19.
Victoria and Albert Museum, London

30 THE GONZAGA VASE   Plate 11
h. 30 cm.
The inscription PROBITAS LAUDATUR under the emblem of the burning bush is found on the reverse of a medal of Gianfrancesco Gonzaga, brother of Federigo Gonzaga, Marquess of Mantua. The emblem of Amor on the chariot drawn by winged horses and the inscription MAI PIU occur on the reverse of a medal of Antonia del Balzo, wife of Gianfrancesco Gonzaga. The vase is a work of Antico's first

period. From the Medagliere Estense, it passed in 1797 to the Liceo Modenese; in 1877 it was put up for sale by the local Intendenza di Finanza, but the sale was prohibited and the bronze was acquired for the Museo Estense.
Bibl: Hermann, in *WJ*, XXVIII, p. 233; Planiscig, *PBI*, pl. CI, fig. 172.
Museo Estense, Modena

31 VENUS (or ATROPOS). Black patination
h. 30 cm.
The model, which is adapted from an antique Venus Victrix, is known through versions in the Kunsthistorisches Museum, Vienna, and the Ashmolean Museum, Oxford. The figure is generally regarded as a Venus; the handle of a pair of scissors is, however, held in the right hand and the end of a distaff in the left. The circlet on the head does not occur in the Vienna bronze.
Coll: Beit (bequeathed by Sir Otto Beit, 1931).
Bibl: Bode, *Catalogue of the Collection of Pictures and Bronzes in the Possession of Mr Otto Beit*, 1913, No. 281, p. 60 (as Antico); Hermann, in *Jahrbuch der Kunsthistorischen Sammlungen des allerhöchsten Kaiserhauses*, XXVIII, 109–10, p. 251; Planiscig, *Bronzeplastiken*, p. 57 (as Antico).
Victoria and Albert Museum, London

32 VENUS
Rough cast not worked up
h. 23·9 cm.
Replica, with variations in the placing of the hands, of a classical figure now in Madrid, in which the right knee rests on the back of a tortoise.
Bibl: Hermann, in *WJ*, XXVIII, 1910, p. 263; Planiscig, *Riccio*, 1927, p. 425; Planiscig, *PBI*, pl. C; Catalogo De Rinaldis, p. 371, No. 427.
Museo Nazionale di Capodimonte, Naples

33 VENUS FELIX
h. 26 cm.
Trial cast, not worked up, for the bronze in Vienna. The position of the left hand differs in the two versions: in that in Vienna it is stretched vertically upwards grasping some object which is now lost, while in the present version it is extended horizontally as if balancing an object on its palm.
Bibl: Hermann, in *WJ*, XXVIII, pp. 247–8;

Planiscig, *Bronzeplastiken*, p. 56, No. 100 (for Vienna version).
Museo Nazionale di Capodimonte, Naples

MANTUAN (late fifteenth century)

34 THE MARTELLI MIRROR. Light brown surface, parcel gilt and inlaid with gold and silver, backed with a steel plate
h. (overall) 22·9 cm., dia. (relief only) 17·3 cm.
The mirror was purchased with a traditional attribution to Donatello, which is accepted by Bode but has otherwise been universally dismissed. The relief on the front is frequently encountered as a plaquette, and individual plaquettes of the two single figures also exist in some numbers; one of these, in the British Museum, has on the reverse the arms of Pope Sixtus IV, and provides a *terminus ante quem* (1484) for the making of the mirror. The mirror is a synthesis of motifs drawn from antique gems, which appear to have been copied in the Medusa head on the handle, the Priapic term, and the figures of the Satyr and Bacchante, and possibly also in the female mask beneath. Milk is pressed by the Bacchante into a rhyton which has a close parallel in an Achaemenid rhyton in the British Museum (for this see Dalton, *The Treasure of the Oxus*, 1926, pl. XXII). The inscription reads: NATVRA FOVET QVAE NECESSITAS VRGET (Nature encourages what necessity requires), and the relief seems to have been planned as an allegory of reproduction in which natural instinct is presented as a stimulus towards the fulfilment of a necessary law. The style and facture of the Mirror suggests an origin in Mantua in the circle of Antico, and it is perhaps the work of the author of a number of small plaquettes signed IO. F. F. (Giovanni Francesco Ruberti).
Coll: Martelli, Florence (purchased 1863).
Bibl: Fortnum, pp. 58–9 (as not by Donatello); Molinier, I, pp. 15–16 (as not by Donatello); Bode, *Denkmäler*, pp. 27–8, pl. 91A (as Donatello); Maclagan, *Catalogue of Italian Plaquettes*, 1924, p. 11 (as not by Donatello, perhaps *c.* 1500); Planiscig, in *Zeitschrift für Bildende Kunst*, LXIV, 1930–1931, p. 76 (as Desiderio da Firenze); Seymour de Ricci, *Dreyfus*, I, p. 6, No. 3.
Victoria and Albert Museum, London

NORTH ITALIAN (early sixteenth century)

35 BUST OF A MAN

h. 12 cm.

One of the finest Renaissance derivations from a classical portrait bust. Presumably made in Mantua in the circle of Antico.

Bibl: Bode, *IBS*, II, p. cvii; Planiscig, *PBI*, pl. CIII.

Museo Estense, Modena

36 MARSYAS   Plate 5

h. 35 cm.

After the antique (for the antique original see Reinach, *Répertoire*, I, 407, and elsewhere). The subject was treated in the Renaissance by a number of different artists, and the bronzes of the subject appear to be based on a number of different classical originals. Despite the notable differences between the various versions, all of them were at one time ascribed to Antonio del Pollajuolo.

Bibl: Venturi, in *Le Gallerie Nazionale Italiane*, 1896, p. 98;

Bode, *IBS*, II, p. 7, pl. XCV.

Museo Estense, Modena

37 BUST OF A WOMAN

h. 17·5 cm.

Inspired by the antique, possibly by a head of Faustina, but interpreted freely in a manner that recalls the tradition of the Lombardi in Venice.

Bibl: Bode, *IBS*, II, p. cviii.

Museo Estense, Modena

PADUA

BARTOLOMEO BELLANO
(b. Padua c. 1435–d. Padua 1496/7)

38 ST JEROME

h. 25 cm.

The attribution to Bellano of this magnificent bronze is based on its relationship to the documented reliefs in the choir of the Santo at Padua. It is suggested by Landais that the bronze may have been among the 'molte cose piccole di marmo e di bronzo' conjecturally made by Bellano for Pope Paul II.

Coll: Piot, Dreyfus.

Bibl: Bode, *IBS*, I, p. 21, pl. XXI (as Bellano); Planiscig, *Riccio*, 1927, p. 43 (as Bellano); Planiscig, *PBI*, pl. XXXVIII, fig. 60 (as Bellano); Landais, *Les Bronzes Italiens de la Renaissance*, 1958, pp. 40, 113, pl. IX (as attributed to Bellano).

Musée du Louvre, Paris

39 GRAZING OX

h. 18 cm., w. 13 cm.

Listed in the catalogue of the Mantova Benavides collection made by Andrea Mantova Benavides in 1695 (MS. in the Biblioteca Civica in Padua) as a work of Pietro Bellano [*sic*]. It was later in the library of S. Giovanni di Verdara, Padua, and subsequently passed to the Biblioteca Marciana, Venice, the Museo Archeologico, and finally to the Ca d'Oro.

Bibl: Frizzoni, *Notizia d'opere di disegno pubblicata da D. Jacopo Morelli*, 1884, pp. 68–9; Bode, in *Archivio Storico dell'Arte*, IV, 1891, p. 404; Planiscig, *Riccio*, 1927, pp. 59–61 (as Bellano).

Ca d'Oro, Venice

40 THREE HORSES

23 × 23 cm.

Provenance as for No. 40. The catalogue of Andrea Mantova Benavides mentions it with a fantastic and incredible attribution to Tiziano Aspetti.

Bibl: Frizzoni, *Notizia d'opere di disegno pubblicata da D. Jacopo Morelli*, 1884, pp. 68–9– Bode, in *Archivio Storico dell'Arte*, IV, 1891, p. 404; Planiscig, *Riccio*, 1927, p. 63 (as Bellano); *Decorative Arts of the Italian Renaissance*, Detroit, 1958, p. 105 (as Riccio).

Ca d'Oro, Venice

41 THE RAPE OF EUROPA

h. 21·5 cm.

A group in the same style in Budapest bears some relation to the art of Bertoldo. The bull is a free derivation from the antique.

Bibl: Bode, *IBS*, I, pl. XXXV (as Riccio); Planiscig, *Riccio*, 1927, pp. 59–61 (as Bellano); Planiscig, *PBI*, pl. XLI (as Bellano).

Museo Nazionale, Florence

42 THE MOUNTAIN OF HELL. Dark patination
h. 26 cm., diameter of base 25 cm.
Harpy at top broken; other figures missing.
Lid of a perfume burner, of a type best known
through two bronzes by Riccio formerly in the
Figdor collection (now destroyed). The imagery
derives from Ovid's description of the visit of
Juno to the underworld (*Metamorphoses*, IV,
447–63), and individual figures are related to
those in an illustration in a Venice edition of the
Metamorphoses (1477). The bronze lacks the
figures of Alcestis, Hercules and Sisyphus, which
are, however, represented in a mid-sixteenth
century derivative in the Museum (A.63-1953).
The mouths and eyes are bored to emit smoke.
A coarse version of the model is in the Stift-
museum at Heiligenkreuz.
Bibl: Pope-Hennessy, in *Burlington Magazine*,
XCVI, 1954, pp. 9–13 (as Bellano); Bode, *IBS*,
I, p. 22, pl. XXV, XXVI (Figdor bronzes as
Bellano); Planiscig, *Riccio*, 1927, p. 77 (Figdor
bronzes as early Riccio).
Victoria and Albert Museum, London

PADUAN (late fifteenth century)

43 A DAMNED SOUL. Solid cast. Dense black lacquer
h. 14·3 cm.
In style and iconography the figure is related to a
bronze in Vienna showing a woman tormented
by serpents emerging from the mouth of a
monster. Both are associable with the Mountains
of Hell and the early activity of Riccio.
Coll: Barsanti.
Bibl: Pollak, *Raccolta Alfredo Barsanti*, Rome,
1924, No. 42, pl. XX; Planiscig, *Riccio*, 1927,
p. 95; *PBI*, XX, XIII, fig. 54; Santangelo, p. 30,
fig. 29.
Museo di Palazzo Venezia, Rome

44 INKSTAND WITH VULCAN AT THE FORGE. Black
lacquer over a natural dark brown patina. The
hammer is missing, and a vase for ink has been
substituted for the anvil.
h. 20·8 cm.
The prototype from which the bronze derives
was formerly in the collection of Martin Le Roy
in Paris, and the bronze may be attributed to the
author of the Mountains of Hell formerly in the
Figdor collection.
Coll: Barsanti.
Bibl: Pollak, *Raccolta Alfredo Barsanti*, Rome,
1924, No. 13, fig. 25; Planiscig, *Riccio*, 1927,
pp. 96, 477, No. 6, fig. 92; Santangelo, p. 28,
fig. 25.
Museo di Palazzo Venezia, Rome

ANDREA BRIOSCO called RICCIO
(b. Padua *c.* 1470/5–d. Padua 1532)

45 ST MARTIN AND THE BEGGAR   Plate 18
h. 74 cm., w. 53·5 cm.
The relief comes from the church of the Servi,
Venice (suppressed 1812), together with four
other reliefs by Riccio, and the tabernacle doors
ascribed to Desiderio da Firenze (No. 76). The
work is not precisely datable, but is distinct from
the group of works executed by Riccio for the
Altar of the Holy Cross in the same church.
Bibl: Planiscig, *Riccio*, 1927, pp. 234, 479, No. 36,
fig. 268.
Ca d'Oro, Venice

46 SPHINX. Dense black patination. Shallow base
raised on naturalistic feet cast separately from
main figure
h. 48·5 cm.
This and the companion figure (No. 47), which
were possibly cast as firedogs, depend from the
four sphinxes at the base of the Paschal Candlestick in S. Antonio at Padua (1507–1516). They
are identified by Planiscig with two Sphinxes
recorded in the inventory of the Obizzi collection
at Catajo in 1806, which were later in the
Estensische Kunstsammlung at Vienna, where
they were replaced between 1870 and 1879 by
copies. The arms on the medallions round the
necks of the two figures have not been identified.
Coll: Salting.
Bibl: Bode, *IBS*, I, p. 30, pl. LVIII (as Riccio);
Planiscig, *Riccio*, 1927, pp. 251–2, 482 (as Riccio);
Planiscig, *PBI*, pl. LVI, fig. 85 (as Riccio).
Victoria and Albert Museum, London

47 SPHINX. Dense black patination. Shallow base
raised on naturalistic feet cast separately from
main figure
h. 48·5 cm.
See No. 47.
Victoria and Albert Museum, London

48 WARRIOR ON HORSEBACK. Black patination partly
rubbed off, revealing reddish-brown bronze.
Rider cast separately from horse. Both legs on
the right side broken and repaired in metal
h. 34 cm.   Plate 16

The model, of which this version is the autograph
original, seems to have enjoyed great popularity,
and exists in inferior versions in the Liechtenstein
collection, Vaduz, the Wernher collection at
Luton Hoo, the Beit collection, in Berlin and
elsewhere. In the derivatives the horse of the
present bronze is replaced by a conventional

horse based on the classical bronze horses on St Mark's.

Coll: Spitzer, Salting.

Bibl: Bode, *IBS*, I, p. 16, pl. XXIX ('the only specimen executed by Riccio himself'); Planiscig, *Riccio*, 1927, pp. 203–7; Planiscig, *PBI*, pl. LIV, fig. 82 (both as Riccio).

Victoria and Albert Museum, London

49 SEATED PAN. Dark patination   Plate 17
h. 19·3 cm.

One of Riccio's most beautiful bronzes, the Pan, which exists only in a single version, is regarded by Bode as a pair to the figure of a sleeping nymph in Berlin, conjecturally identified as Syrinx. This conjunction is unconvincing. A related bronze is in the Walters Art Gallery at Baltimore.

Bibl: Bode, *IBS*, I, pl. XXXIII (as Riccio); Planiscig, *Riccio*, 1927, pp. 423–4 (as Riccio); Planiscig, *PBI*, pl. LXXXII, fig. 137 (as Riccio).

Ashmolean Museum, Oxford

50 SLEEPING NYMPH. Dark brown patination
h. 18·2 cm.

Version of a model previously known from a single example in Berlin, tentatively identified by Bode as Syrinx and regarded by him as a pair to the Oxford Pan (No. 49). There can be little doubt that the bronze was made as part of a larger group. The example in Berlin has a flat rectangular bronze base and a tree-trunk supporting the right arm.

Bibl: Bode, *IBS*, I, p. 26, pl. XXXIII (Berlin bronze as Riccio); Planiscig, *Riccio*, 1927, pp. 420–1, fig. 506 (Berlin bronze as Riccio).

Private Collection

51 THE PUNISHMENT OF PAN. Dark brown patination
h. 17·4 cm.

The group appears to have been made as the lid of an inkstand or other receptacle. Versions of the three figures exist singly. Planiscig records a gilded variant of the complete group without the figure of Cupid in the Boucquet-Bournet de Verron collection, Paris. The independent single figures are larger in size, and it is possible that the present group is a reduction from a larger autograph original. The group is explained by Bode as an allegory of the restraint of passion, and by Planiscig as the punishment of Pan. The female figure certainly represents Pomona, but it is not certain that the satyr should be identified as Pan.

Bibl: Bode, *IBS*, I, p. 29, fig. 22 (as Riccio);

Planiscig, *Riccio*, 1927, pp. 252–4 (as Riccio).

Ashmolean Museum, Oxford

52 DEMON
h. 21·4 cm.

A very early work, related to the Hecate in Berlin.

Bibl: Venturi, in *Bollettino d'Arte*, IV, 1910, p. 353; Planiscig, *Riccio*, 1927, pp. 95, 477, No. 5, figs. 88–9 (as Riccio); Planiscig, *PBI*, pl. XLVI, fig. 70 (as Riccio).

Museo Civico, Belluno

53 A FAT MAN
h. 17 cm.

The figure is represented naked with a skullcap on the head. A very similar version in Vienna is crowned with vine-leaves. A late work.

Bibl: Planiscig, *Riccio*, 1927, pp. 396, 481, No. 72, fig. 494.

Museo del Castello Sforzesco, Milan

54 RAM. Black lacquer. Surface chiselled
h. 17 cm.

Other examples of the model with the sacrificial wreath and the tufts of wool left on the body after shearing are in the museums at Brunswick and Vienna. A version formerly in the Figdor collection, Vienna, lacks the wreath. Simplified workshop replicas are frequently encountered.

Coll: Barsanti.

Bibl: Planiscig, *Riccio*, 1927, pp. 197, 486, No. 144, fig. 215; Santangelo, p. 29, fig. 63.

Museo di Palazzo Venezia, Rome

55 SATYR AND SATYRESS. Dark patination partly rubbed   Plate 12
h. 23·2 cm.

The bronze, which was presented to the Museum by the National Art-Collections Fund, is the only complete autograph version of a model of which a coarse studio variant exists in the Szepmuveszetimuseum at Budapest and a good version of the Satyress alone is at Brunswick. A draped seat in the Cleveland Museum of Art with, at the back, a putto climbing a tree (wrongly designated as an ink-stand) perhaps formed the base of the present group.

Bibl: Planiscig, *Riccio*, 1927, figs. 291–2 (for Brunswick and Budapest bronzes); *PBI*, pl. LXXVI, fig. 124 (for base).

Victoria and Albert Museum, London

56 SHEPHERD WITH A GOAT   Plate 14
h. 26 cm.

The same pastoral motif occurs in the lower

right-hand corner of the relief of David dancing before the Ark in the Santo at Padua. The present figure is a late work, datable around 1530, and related to the terracotta St Henry in S. Canziano, Padua. No other version of the bronze survives.

Coll: Carrand.

Bibl: Planiscig, *Riccio*, 1927, pp. 193, 480, No. 60, fig. 212.

Museo Nazionale, Florence

57 ABUNDANCE   Plate 15
    h. 23 cm.

Headdresses of the same kind occur in numerous terracottas and bronzes of Riccio's maturity and late period. No other version of this bronze is known.

Coll: Carrand.

Bibl: Planiscig, *Riccio*, 1927, pp. 258, 480, No. 61, fig. 290.

Museo Nazionale, Florence

58 SEATED SATYR   Plate 13
    h. 20 cm.

Designed as a combined candlestick and ink-stand, the figure was originally set on a triangular base. It does not exist in any other version.

Coll: Carrand.

Bibl: Planiscig, *Riccio*, 1927, pp. 355, 485, No. 123, fig. 434; Planiscig, *PBI*, pl. LXVII.

Museo Nazionale, Florence

59 SATYR SUPPORTING A SHELL. Natural reddish brown patination, with traces of black lacquer
    h. 23·3 cm.

Autograph example of a model which was often reproduced with variations in Riccio's workshop. The sea-shell is a natural cast.

Coll: Barsanti.

Bibl: Pollak, *Raccolta Alfredo Barsanti*, Rome, 1924, No. 9, pl. IV; Planiscig, *Riccio*, 1927, pp. 330, 483, No. 100, fig. 380; Santangelo, p. 29, fig. 31.

Museo di Palazzo Venezia, Rome

60 BUST OF A WOMAN
    h. 13 cm.

The execution is extremely precise and is reminiscent of that of a statuette of a naked woman holding a cymbal in the Martin Le Roy collection in Paris. No other version of the bronze is known.

Coll: Carrand.

Bibl: Planiscig, *Riccio*, 1927, pp. 263, 486, No. 140, fig. 294.

Museo Nazionale, Florence

61 GROTESQUE DOOR-KNOCKER WITH A DEVIL CLUTCHING THE HEAD OF A BULL. Dark brown patination
    h. 25·1 cm.

The knocker belongs to a group of bronze door-knockers by Riccio, of which related models are recorded in the former Pourtalès collection and in the Kunstgewerbe Museum, Berlin. The present model exists in two variants in the former Wittman collection, Budapest, and the former Newall collection. The head of the devil faces in the opposite direction to that on the Wittman knocker.

Bibl: Planiscig, *Riccio*, 1927, pp. 361–3, 489 (for Berlin, Pourtalès and Wittman knockers) (as Riccio); Planiscig, *PBI*, pl. LXXX, fig. 132 (Wittman knocker as Riccio).

Mr Francis Stonor, London

62 LAMP IN THE FORM OF A SPHINX
    h. 20·5 cm.

Lower part mutilated. The lamp is now mounted on a cock's claw. The cover is derived from the sphinxes which support the tomb-chest of the Della Torre monument in Verona. A workshop replica in Florence has its original foot but lacks the lid; another variant, converted into a flask, was in the Kauffman and Weininger collections, Berlin.

Bibl: Planiscig, *Riccio*, 1927, pp. 379, 489, No. 184, fig. 475.

Museo Estense, Modena

63 OIL LAMP WITH THE MASK OF A BEARDED MAN. Dark patination
    h. 23·7 cm.

The lamp, which is fully autograph, also exists in a second version formerly in the Simon collection, Berlin. The male mask is reminiscent of those on the base of the Paschal Candlestick at Padua.

Coll: Salting.

Bibl: Planiscig, *Riccio*, 1927, p. 380; Planiscig, *PBI*, pl. LIX, fig. 92 (both as Riccio).

Victoria and Albert Museum, London

64 OIL LAMP IN THE FORM OF A BOAT. Dark patination
    h. 13·2 cm., l. 21 cm.

Tips of scrolls broken at base. Lid cast separately from body of lamp.

One of a group of three oil lamps, existing in single versions only, of which the second and third are in the former Gustave Rothschild collection, Paris, and the Frick collection, New York. The three lamps are some of Riccio's finest surviving decorative works. The iconography of the present example is unexplained; it is, how-

ever, clear that the youth blowing a sail in the medallion on one side of the lamp, is contrasted with the obese figure on the opposite side, and that the latter corresponds with figures of Sloth in the Mantegna engraving of Virtus Combusta and the Minerva expelling the Vices in the Louvre.
Bibl: Bode, *IBS*, I, pl. LIII, fig. 3; Planiscig, *Riccio*, 1927, p. 273 (both as Riccio).
Victoria and Albert Museum, London

65 LAMP IN THE FORM OF A GROTESQUE HEAD
h. 7 cm.
Workshop replicas, always with some variations, are frequently encountered. An example in the Museo Nazionale, Florence, is more than twice as large (h. 17 cm.), but of inferior quality.
Bibl: Planiscig, *Riccio*, 1927, pp. 176, 488, No. 167, fig. 183.
Museo Estense, Modena

66 VASE
h. 10 cm.
Decorated with bucraniums, masks and putti. With a single handle.
Bibl: Planiscig, *Riccio*, 1927, p. 489, No. 200.
Museo Nazionale, Florence

67 THE ENTOMBMENT
h. 10 cm., w. 14·5 cm.
The initials G.B.F. are incised in the upper part. An example, formerly in the Dreyfus collection and now in the National Gallery of Art, Washington (Kress collection), has an R cast on the back. Other examples are recorded in Berlin and in the former von Benda collection, Vienna.
Bibl: Planiscig, *Riccio*, 1927, pp. 287, 479, No. 40; de Ricci, *The Gustave Dreyfus Collection: Reliefs and Plaquettes*, 1931, p. 94 (for Dreyfus example and list of other versions).
Ca d'Oro, Venice

68 THE ENTOMBMENT
h. 11·8 cm., w. 16·7 cm.
Inscribed on the sarcophagus: QVEM.TOTVS.NON/ CAP. ORB. IN HAC./TVMBA CLAVDIT. Examples without the inscription occur more frequently, but some of these are also autograph.
Bibl: Molinier, *Les Plaquettes*, p. 118, No. 221; Planiscig, *Riccio*, 1927, p. 492, No. 228.
Ca d'Oro, Venice

69 DIDO. Natural dark brown patination
h. 15 cm., w. 10 cm.
Similar to a plaquette in the British Museum. There is a weaker replica, circular in shape, in the Museo Correr in Venice. The figurative scheme depends from an engraving by Marcantonio Raimondi.
Coll: Donà delle Rose.
Exh: Kleinkunst der Italienischen Renaissance, Vienna, Kunsthistorisches Museum, 1936, No. 35.
Bibl: Lorenzetti-Planiscig, *Donà delle Rose Catalogue,* 1934, No. 239; Planiscig, in *Dedalo,* XII, 1932, p. 921.
H. E. Giacinto Auriti, Rome

70 TOBIAS
h. 7 cm.
Workshop replica of a model of which other versions with variations exist in Vienna and Berlin.
Bibl: Planiscig, *Riccio*, 1927, p. 200, fig. 224 (as Riccio).
Museo Nazionale, Florence

71 SEATED SATYR
h. 20 cm.
The figure is drinking out of a cup. Workshop replica, of which the original is in the Kunsthistorisches Museum, Vienna.
Bibl: Planiscig, *Riccio*, 1927, p. 484, No. 115; Moschetti, *Il Museo Civico di Padova*, 1938, p. 221; Ferrari, in *Bollettino del Museo Civico di Padova*, XVII–XVIII, 1934–1939, p. 274.
Museo Civico, Padua

SEVERO DA RAVENNA
(Active in Padua *c.* 1500)

72 PLUTO WITH A DRAGON
h. 55·5 cm.
An ink-stand in the form of a dragon, formerly in the Robert Mayer collection in Vienna, now in the Blumka collection, New York, signed O SEVERI RA, enables the present bronze and other bronzes formerly attributed to the Master of the Dragon to be given to Severo da Ravenna. Other complete examples, from independent models, exist in the Kunsthistorisches Museum, Vienna, and in the Frick collection, New York. This last is much superior to the present bronze.
Bibl: Planiscig, in *WJ*, n.s. IX, 1935, pp. 75 ff.; *The Frick Collection*, V, 1953, pp. 28–30 (full biography).
Museo Nazionale, Florence

Attributed to SEVERO DA RAVENNA

73 NEGRO BOY MOUNTED ON A GOAT. Dark brown patination   Plate 20
h. 21·6 cm.
This extremely distinguished bronze differs from

the autograph bronzes of Riccio both in the casting and the surface working. Planiscig ascribes it to the author of a statue of a chained Negro in Vienna, and associates both tentatively with the work of Severo da Ravenna. The Vienna and Birmingham bronzes are undoubtedly by the same hand.

Coll: McCann.

Exh: Detroit, 1958–1959, No. 249 (as school of Riccio).

Bibl: Planiscig, in *WJ*, n.s. XIII, 1944, pp. 249–50; Sewter, in *The Connoisseur*, 1949, p. 24 (as Riccio).

The Barber Institute of Fine Arts, Birmingham

DESIDERIO DA FIRENZE
(Documented, Padua, 1532–1545)

74 VOTING URN. Traces of gilding. Cast in three parts
h. 51 cm.
Executed for the Consiglio of the Comune of Padua between March 7, 1532, and February 8, 1533. The document recording payments for the urn is preserved in the Biblioteca Comunale in Padua.

Bibl: Moschetti, in *Bollettino del Museo Civico di Padova*, n.s. III, 1927, p. 148; Moschetti, *Il Museo Civico di Padova*, 1938, p. 219; Planiscig, in *Zeitschrift für bildende Kunst*, LXIV, 1930–1931, p. 71.

Museo Civico, Padua

75 STANDING SATYR. Rich brown lacquer partly rubbed, revealing light brown natural patination
h. 27·3 cm.
The figure, which exists in a single version, is by the same hand as a Satyr drinking from a Cup and a Satyr leaning on a Tree-trunk in the Kunsthistorisches Museum, Vienna, all of which are ascribed by Planiscig, on the strength of the documented voting urn from the Museo Civico at Padua (No. 74), to Desiderio da Firenze. The Satyr seems to be represented gazing down at a sleeping nymph, and must originally have formed part of a two-figure group; there is no reason to suppose with Planiscig that it held a shell or vase.

Coll: Lederer.

Bibl: Planiscig, *VB*, pp. 400–1.

Victoria and Albert Museum, London

76 TABERNACLE DOORS
88 × 22 cm.
The doors, which represent the Glorification of the Cross, were made for a tabernacle containing a relic of the Holy Cross given to the church of the Servi in Venice in 1492 by Girolamo Donati.

The altar dedicated to it was conceived subsequently and may have resulted from a bequest after the death of the donor in Rome on October 20, 1511. The four scenes of the Invention of the Cross, which were part of the altar and are now also in the Ca d'Oro, are certainly by Riccio. As Moschetti has observed, the doors of the tabernacle are by another artist, who may be identified with Riccio's collaborator Desiderio da Firenze.

Bibl: Planiscig, *Riccio*, 1927, pp. 230 ff.; Moschetti, in *Bollettino del Museo Civico di Padova*, n.s., III, 1927, pp. 143 ff.

Ca d'Oro, Venice

Attributed to DESIDERIO DA FIRENZE

77 BELL. Handle missing
h. 10 cm.
Studio work. The arms (which include two snakes) have not been identified. A version of the model in Berlin bears the arms of Madruzzo of Trent, and another in the Frick collection, New York, those of Doria.

Bibl: Nicodemi, in *Dedalo*, I, 1920–1921, p. 466; Planiscig, in *Zeitschrift für bildende Kunst*, LXIV, 1930–1931, p. 75.

Musei Civici, Brescia

78 BELL
h. 16·6 cm.
On the handle is a seated figure of St Peter holding a scroll inscribed: ET ERIT TANDEM. The arms have not been identified.

Bibl: Nicodemi, in *Dedalo*, I, 1920–1921, 466.

Musei Civici, Brescia

79 PERFUME BURNER. Dark brown patina
h. 40·5 cm.
The perfume burner consists of three separate parts, placed one above the other. Against the triangular ara-shaped base are squatting satyrs, on the panels are reliefs after Moderno. The second part consists of a column, grooved bands and sphinxes. The third part consists of a vessel surmounted by Mars. Similar examples in the museum at Brunswick, the Metropolitan Museum, New York (Blumenthal collection), and at Chatsworth.

Coll: It is possible that the piece comes from the collection of Comte de Seignelai and was afterwards in the collection of the Earl of Oxford.

Exh: Frank Partridge, London, June 1956, No. 60; acquired in 1957.

Bibl: Montfaucon, *Antiquité Expliquée*, Suppl. I (1724), p. 139, pls. 50/52; Planiscig, *Riccio*, 1927,

fig. 373 (Brunswick brazier as workshop of Riccio); Planiscig, *PBI*, fig. 134 (Blumenthal perfume burner as Riccio).
Rijksmuseum, Amsterdam

PADUAN (first half of the sixteenth century)

80 BOWL
h. 23·3 cm.
The ornament and technique recall the candle-sticks, decorated bases and other objects for practical use which were produced in Padua and Venice under the influence of Desiderio da Firenze and the late tradition of the Lombardi.
Bibl: Planiscig, *PBI*, pl. XCII, fig. 157.
Museo Nazionale, Florence

81 MELEAGER (or ADONIS). Dark patination; casting defective
h. 20·5 cm.
The bronze exists in a number of versions (Metropolitan Museum, New York; former Figdor and former Heseltine collections). Like the present version, an example formerly in the Benda collection has as its counterpart a seated figure of Venus and Cupid. It has repeatedly been questioned whether the two bronzes were produced in the same studio, since the male figure is conventionally dated to the late fifteenth century and the female figure is undoubtedly of later date. The thinness of the casting in the surviving versions of the Meleager constitutes an argument against an early dating, and the probability is that the two figures, despite certain discrepancies, belong together, and were made towards the middle of the century. The nude figure is variously described as representing the sleeping Meleager and the dying Adonis. If, as is likely, the expression of the companion figure denotes lamentation, the second explanation is likely to be correct.
Coll: Salting.
Bibl: Bode, *IBS*, III, pp. 13–14 (first quarter of sixteenth century or even later); Planiscig, *Riccio*, 1927, pp. 109–10; Planiscig, *PBI*, p. 13, pl. XXX, fig. 50 (both as Paduan, late fifteenth century); Tietze-Conrat, in *WJ*, 1918, pp. 44–51 (later dating); Maclagan, in *The Frick Collection*, V, 1953, pp. 46–8 (best analysis of model).
Victoria and Albert Museum, London

82 VENUS. Dark patination
h. 20·5 cm.
See No. 81.
Coll: Salting.
Victoria and Albert Museum, London

FRANCESCO DA SANT'AGATA
(Active Padua, 1520)

83 HERCULES. Black patination   Plate 19
h. 23·5 cm.
The bronze, which also exists in an inferior version in the Louvre, is related in posture to a boxwood Hercules in the Wallace Collection, London, signed OPVS. FRANCISCI. AVRIFICIS, which is described by Scardeone in the collection of Marc Antonio Massimo at Padua, and is stated by him to have been carved in 1520. A boxwood statuette of St Sebastian by the same hand in Berlin corresponds with a bronze statuette in the Frick collection, New York. It is assumed by Bode that the Oxford bronze is a cast from a wax model made by Sant'Agata in preparation for the boxwood carving. The heads, of the bronze and boxwood are, however, markedly different in type, and it is by no means certain that they are by a single hand. Landais supposes that the boxwood was copied from the bronze, and that the latter was made by an unidentified Paduan sculptor about 1500; the first part of this theory may be correct, but so early a dating is not consistent with what we know of the development of Paduan bronze casting.
Bibl: Bode, *IBS*, I, pp. 40–1, pl. LXXVIII (as Francesco da Sant'Agata); Planiscig, *VB*, pp. 300–1 (as Francesco da Sant'Agata); Planiscig, *PBI*, pl. CXXVIII, fig. 224 (as Francesco da Sant'Agata); Landais, *Les Bronzes italiens de la Renaissance*, 1958, p. 42.
Ashmolean Museum, Oxford

84 FAUN PLAYING A DOUBLE FLUTE
h. 32·5 cm.
Versions of the model without the flute exist in Berlin, the Frick collection, New York, and elsewhere. It belongs to a group of bronzes of male nude figures in movement, of which one of the most notable is a Niobid figure in the Wallace Collection, London, ascribed by Bode to Francesco da Sant'Agata. There is a strong case for attributing the present bronze and the related models to the same hand as the Oxford Hercules (No. 83), but the connection of the entire group with Sant'Agata is hypothetical. The doubts expressed by Maclagan as to the autograph character of the known versions of the present model appear, at least in the case of the Louvre bronze, to be unjustified.
Bibl: Bode, *IBS*, I, pl. LXXX (Berlin version as Sant'Agata); Planiscig, *VB*, p. 302 (Frick version as Sant'Agata); Planiscig, *PBI*, pl. CXXIX, fig. 227 (Louvre version as Sant'Agata); Maclagan, in *The Frick Collection*, V, 1953, p. 51

(Frick version as workshop of Sant'Agata).
Musée du Louvre, Paris

Style of FRANCESCO DA SANT'AGATA

85 MALE FIGURE WITH ARMS RAISED
h. 21·5 cm.
Based on the antique, possibly on a figure of Narcissus, the bronze survives in a number of versions, of which the best known are in the Wallace Collection, the Louvre, and the Ehem. Staatliche Museen, Berlin. A variant, probably adapted from the same classical original, exists in the Museo Nazionale, Florence. The attribution to Francesco da Sant'Agata is due to Bode.
Bibl: Bode, *IBS*, I, pl. LXXX (for Wallace collection bronze); Bode, in *Kunst und Künstler*, VI, 1907, pp. 61–8; Mann, *Wallace Collection Catalogues, Sculpture*, 1931, pp. 31–2 (for Wallace collection bronze).
Mr John Bryson, Oxford

86 FEMALE FIGURE WITH ARMS RAISED
h. 20 cm.
Apparently based on the antique, the figure forms a pair to No. 85 (*q.v.*).
Mr John Bryson, Oxford

VENICE

VENETIAN (last quarter of the fifteenth century)

87 CHILD WITH HOUR-GLASS AND SKULL. Solid cast. Dark patination partly rubbed
h. 12·5 cm., l. 13·5 cm.
Round the edge of the base is the inscription:
IL. TEMP. PASSA. E LA MORTO. VEN.
PAR(A)TO. SIA. CHI. NON. FA. BEN.
FAC(I)AMO. MAL. E SPERANDO. I(N). BE(N).
IL. TEMPO. P(A)SSA. E LA MO(RTO). VE(N).
(Time is passing, and Death is coming; let him who is not doing good be prepared; we do evil and we hope for the best; Time is passing and Death is coming.) No other version of the model is known. For the subject compare the reverse of a medallic self-portrait by Giovanni Boldù (Hill, No. 421).
Coll: Oppenheimer (sale 15/6/1936, No. 122). Presented by the National Art-Collections Fund.
Bibl: *BFAC*, 1912, No. 5, pp. 56–7 (as Florentine or Paduan, late fifteenth century); Bode, *IBS*, III, pl. CCXLIX, fig. 3 (as Paduan, early sixteenth century); Janson, in *Art Bulletin*, XIX, 1937, pp. 423–49 (exhaustive discussion of iconography).
Victoria and Albert Museum, London

VENETIAN (about 1500)

88 ST JOHN THE BAPTIST. Black patination partly rubbed
h. 26 cm.
The bronze is connected by Bode with the small St Jerome (of which an example from Brescia is included in the exhibition, No. 93), and the reliefs of the Barbarigo Altar under a tentative ascription to Antonio Lombardo. Planiscig associates it with the wholly dissimilar bronze statues by Filippo da Gonzate in the Duomo at Parma. The quality of the statuette is superior both to the St Jerome and to the Barbarigo reliefs; it finds a point of reference is the Zen Altar in St Mark's, and may have been made by one of the two artists (Antonio Lombardo and Paolo Savin) responsible for this work. The pose and drapery forms also show affinities with the signed marble statue of the Baptist by Severo da Ravenna in S. Antonio at Padua.
Bibl: Bode, *IBS*, I, p. 39, pl. LXXVII (as Antonio Lombardo?); Planiscig, *PBI*, p. 24, pl. CXII, fig. 195 (as Filippo da Gonzate).
Ashmolean Museum, Oxford

TULLIO LOMBARDO
(b. *c.* 1455–d. Vienna 1582)

89A HEAD OF A GIRL
  B HEAD OF A GIRL
h. 19·4 and 19·9 cm. (each)
The busts constitute a pair. Similar busts occur, usually singly, in the former Spitzer collection, the Wallace Collection, London, Berlin and elsewhere.
Bibl: Bode, *IBS*, I, pl. LXXVI; Venturi, *La Galleria Estense in Modena*, 1882, p. 99; Planiscig, *VB*, p. 254 (as Tullio Lombardo).
Museo Estense, Modena

90 BUST OF A BEARDED MAN. Black patination
h. 15·5 cm.
Round the shoulders hangs a classical tunica of which the two ends are fastened on the right. The bust is related in type to the two female busts from Modena (No. 89).

Bibl: Rijksmuseum, *Catalogus van Beeldhouwerken*, 1915, No. 60.
Rijksmuseum, Amsterdam

MASTER OF THE BARBARIGO ALTAR
(Active *c.* 1515)

91 THE ASSUMPTION OF THE VIRGIN
h. 36 cm., w. 25 cm.
The Master of the Barbarigo Altar, an anonymous artist working in the circle of Antonio and Tullio Lombardo, is so named from the Barbarigo Altar in the Church of the Carità in Venice, from which three reliefs survive. The present relief is one of these. There is documentary evidence that the altar was complete before 1515. The altar was dismantled at the beginning of the nineteenth century, but is recorded in an engraving of 1692 which shows that it also comprised the praying figure of Agostino Barbarigo, now in the sacristy of S. Maria della Salute, and a relief of the Resurrection, now in a corridor of the Scuola di Giovanni Evangelista.
Bibl: Planiscig, *VB*, pp. 209 ff.; Fogolari-Nebbia-Moschini, *La R. Galleria Giorgio Franchetti alla Ca d'Oro*, 1929, 148.
Ca d'Oro, Venice

92 ST JEROME
h. 16 cm.
The bronze is known through a version of somewhat lower quality in the Victoria and Albert Museum, which is rightly given by Planiscig to the Master of the Barbarigo reliefs.
Bibl: Fortnum, p. 15 (London version as recalling the manner of the Lombardi); Bode, *IBS*, p. 39, pl. LXXVII (closely allied to the marble figure of St Jerome by Pietro Lombardo in S. Stefano, Venice, but possibly an early work by Antonio Lombardo); Planiscig, *VB*, p. 214 (as Master of the Barbarigo Reliefs).
Musei Civici, Brescia

VITTOR CAMELIO
(b. Venice *c.* 1460–d. 1537)

93 BATTLE OF THE GIANTS
h. 40 cm., w. 67 cm.
Together with another signed relief of about the same size, the present relief comes from the tomb which Camelio built for himself and his brother Briamonte. The tomb was originally in the cloister, and later in the Church, of the Carità in Venice. A will drawn up by Briamonte in 1539 makes it clear that the monument had been built not long before, and it must therefore date from the last years of Camelio's life. Formerly in the Museo Archeologico, to which the two reliefs came immediately after the dismantling of the tomb in the nineteenth century.
Bibl: Planiscig, *VB*, p. 310; Fogolari-Nebbia-Moschini, *La R. Galleria Giorgio Franchetti alla Ca d'Oro*, 1929, p. 83.
Ca d'Oro, Venice

VENETIAN (first quarter of the sixteenth century)

94 HERCULES AND THE SERPENT   Plate 21
h. 29 cm.
No other example of this bronze is known. The conception differs from that of the bronzes of the same subject after the antique.
Bibl: Planiscig, *PBI*, pl. CXVIII (as Venetian *c.* 1500).
Museo Correr, Venice

95 BUST OF A CHILD
h. 15 cm.
Derivation from the antique. The eyes, which were originally filled with silver or glass paste, are void.
Bibl: Planiscig, *VB*, p. 343, fig. 350.
Museo Correr, Venice

96 BUST OF A CHILD. The eyes enamelled with glass paste
h. 16 cm.
Free derivation from the antique. Related heads are in the Este collection, Vienna, and in the Grassi collection, Florence (formerly).
Bibl: Planiscig, *VB*, p. 344, fig. 353.
Ca d'Oro, Venice

97 PRUDENCE
h. 14·5 cm.
Free derivation from the antique. The figure is shown examining herself in a mirror. Other examples are in Berlin, Vienna and the Museo Correr, Venice.
Bibl: Rizzini, p. 15, No. 56; Nicodemi, in *Dedalo*, I, 1920–1921, p. 466.
Musei Civici, Brescia

LOMBARDY

MAFFEO OLIVIERI
(b. Brescia 1484–d. Brescia 1543/4)

98 MELEAGER. Light brown natural patination
h. 24 cm.
Brought by Planiscig into relation with a statuette of Tubalcain in the Kaiser Friedrich Museum, Berlin. The subsequent discovery of documents relating to the wooden altarpiece at Gandino, and Morassi's researches into the activity of the artist in the region of Brescia, confirm the attribution of the bronze to the Olivieri workshop.
Bibl: Planiscig, in *Dedalo*, XII, 1932, p. 34.
H. E. Giacinto Auriti, Rome

MILANESE (middle of the sixteenth century)

99 GIAN GIACOMO TRIVULZIO
h. 29 cm. (without base)
Sketch for an equestrian monument which, according to the inscription, was designed for the Piazza San Nazaro in Milan. Equestrian bronzes of the same type but in a different style, also commemorating members of the Trivulzio family, are in the Louvre and in the former G. von Benda collection, Vienna.
Bibl: Planiscig, *PBI*, pl. CXVI, fig. 201.
Museo del Castello Sforzesco, Milan

MIDDLE OF THE SIXTEENTH CENTURY AND EARLY SEVENTEENTH CENTURY

FLORENCE

NICCOLO TRIBOLO
(b. Florence 1500–d. Florence 1550)

100 AESOP. Dark patination
h. 32·5 cm.
The bronze, which was perhaps designed as a candlestick, was copied by Valerio Cioli in a marble statue now in the garden at Careggi (near Florence). A second statue at Careggi reproduces the companion bronze of the Dwarf on a Snail in the Louvre. There has been some uncertainty as to the place and date of production of the two bronzes, which are, however, by the same hand as a documented bronze of *Pan* by Tribolo in the Museo Nazionale, Florence.
Bibl: Fortnum, p. 17 (as Florentine, sixteenth century); Bode, *IBS*, III, p. 22, pl. CXLVII (as Italian, *c.* 1520); Planiscig, in *WJ*, XIII, 1944, p. 248 (as Paduan, early sixteenth century); Keutner, in *Kunstgeschichtliche Studien für Hans Kauffmann*, 1956, p. 251n (as Cioli); Pope-Hennessy, in *Burlington Magazine*, CI, 1959, pp. 85–9 (as Tribolo). For the attribution of the Bargello *Pan* see Holderbaum, in *Burlington Magazine*, XCIX, 1957, pp. 336–43.
Victoria and Albert Museum, London

PIERINO DA VINCI
(b. Vinci *c.* 1521–d. Pisa 1554)

101 JEALOUSY. Dark black patination, chiselled
h. 38 cm.
The attribution of the bronze to Pierino da Vinci is due to Kris, and is accepted by Planiscig. No other version of the model is known.
Coll: Marczipani; von Rho; Auspitz; van Beuningen.
Exh: Italiaansche Kunst, Amsterdam, 1934, Stedelijk Museum, No. 925.
Bibl: Braun, *Die Bronzen der Sammlung Guido von Rho, Vienna*, 1908, No. 15 (as Cellini); Kris, in *Pantheon*, 1929, p. 96 (as Pierino da Vinci); Planiscig, *PBI*, pl. CLXXXV, fig. 322 (as Pierino da Vinci); Weinberger, in *Zeitschrift für Bildende Kunst*, LXV, 1931, p. 54 (as seventeenth century); Hannema, *Catalogue of the D. G. van Beuningen Collection*, 1949, p. 193, No. 203 (as Pierino da Vinci).
Museum Boymans-van Beuningen, Rotterdam

102 SAMSON SLAYING TWO PHILISTINES. Dark greenish-black patination
Right arm broken and repaired

h. 35·7 cm.

This bronze exists in a number of versions, and owes its interest to the fact that it is the only small bronze based directly on a model by Michelangelo. Michelangelo's model (which is described by Vasari) was made about 1528 for a projected group of Samson and two Philistines, and has disappeared, but the bronze is also related to a surviving model by Michelangelo for a Hercules and Cacus in the Casa Buonarroti, Florence. There is no record that Pierino da Vinci made a bronze statuette from either of these models, but it is stated by Vasari that when carving the marble Samson and Philistine, which is now in the courtyard of the Palazzo Vecchio, he had access to sketches by Michelangelo. The attribution of the present bronze to Pierino da Vinci is therefore conjectural, and has recently been replaced, in the case of the finest extant version, in the Frick collection, New York, with a hypothetical attribution to Daniele da Volterra, to whom two examples in the Museo Nazionale, Florence, were also at one time ascribed.

Coll: Castiglione, van Beuningen.
Bibl: Supino, in *Miscellanea d'Arte,* I, 1903, pp. 41–3 (Bargello bronze as Daniele da Volterra); Schlosser, in *WJ,* XXXI, 1913, pp. 108–10 (Bargello bronze as Pierino da Vinci); Bode, *IBS,* II, pp. 16–17 (as not by Daniele da Volterra); Stechow, in *PJ,* 1928, pp. 82–92 (Bargello bronze as Pierino da Vinci); Planiscig, *Collezione Castiglione, Catalogo dei Bronzi,* No. 73 (as Pierino da Vinci); Venturi, *Storia,* X-ii, 1936, p. 342 (Bargello bronze as Pierino da Vinci); Hannema, *Catalogue of the D. G. van Beuningen Collection,* 1949, p. 194, No. 205 (as Pierino da Vinci).
Museum Boymans-van Beuningen, Rotterdam

103 SAMSON SLAYING TWO PHILISTINES
h. 36·8 cm.
See No. 102 for a second example of this model.
Bibl: As for No. 102.
Museo Nazionale, Florence

Attributed to PIERINO DA VINCI

104 SAMSON SLAYING A PHILISTINE. Dark patination
h. 44·8 cm.
The model is encountered less frequently than No. 102, from which it derives. The attribution to Pierino da Vinci is unconvincing, and the bronze seems to date from *c.* 1575.
Coll: Castiglione.
Bibl: Planiscig, *Collezione Camillo Castiglione, Catalogo dei Bronzi,* 1923, No. 72 (as Pierino da Vinci); Hannema, *Catalogue of the D. G. van*

Beuningen Collection, 1949, p. 193, No. 204 (as Pierino da Vinci).
Museum Boymans-van Beuningen, Rotterdam

BACCIO BANDINELLI
(b. Florence 1488–d. Florence 1559 or 1560)

105 VENUS WITH A DOVE
h. 37·4 cm.
Signed: Baccius Bandinelli.
Bibl: Planiscig, *PBI,* p. 42, pl. CLXXXIII.
Museo Nazionale, Florence

106 CLEOPATRA
h. 30·7 cm.
Another example exists in the Museo Nazionale, Florence.
Coll: Farnese (Capodimonte).
Bibl: De Rinaldis, p. 372, No. 438.
Museo Nazionale di Capodimonte, Naples

DOMENICO POGGINI
(b. Florence 1520–d. Rome 1590)

107 PLUTO
h. 96 cm.
In 1570 the apartments of Francesco de' Medici in the Palazzo Vecchio in Florence were redecorated and modified under the direction of Vasari. The most notable of them was a Studiolo, designed as a repository of precious objects—jewels, medals, cameos and crystals—arranged in cupboards built into the walls. The programme for the decoration of the room was directly related to its function, and was laid down by Vincenzo Borghini. It represented the four elements, and in addition to the paintings covering the walls comprised eight bronze mythological figures, two for the element of Earth (Pluto and Ops), two for Water (Venus Anadyomene and Amphitrite), two for Air (Juno and Aeolus), and two for Fire (Apollo and Vulcan). Soon after they were installed—about 1580—the eight figures were moved from their niches in the Studiolo to the Uffizi; they were replaced in their original positions in 1910–11. The figures were entrusted to eight different sculptors. Those not included in the exhibition are by Ammanati (*Ops,* executed in 1572–1573), Stoldo Lorenzi (*Amphitrite,* completed in 1573) Vincenzo Danti (*Venus Anadyomene,* not documented but described as a work of Danti by Pascoli), and Elia Candido (*Aeolus,* perhaps from a model by Giovanni Bologna, signed and dated 1573). A mistaken attempt has been made to ascribe Danti's *Venus Anadyomene* to Ammanati, and Ammanati's *Ops* to Calamech. Payments for the

Pluto of Domenico Poggini run from February 1572 to July 1573. A nineteenth-century variant of this figure is in the Victoria and Albert Museum.
Bibl: Pelli Benciveni, *Saggio storico della Real Galleria di Firenze*, 1779, p. 145; Gotti, *Le Gallerie di Firenze*, 1872, p. 61; Poggi, in *Il Marzocco*, II–XII, 1910, p. 000; Jahn Rusconi, in *Les Arts*, X, 1911, fasc. 110, pp. 1–7; Lensi, *Il Palazzo Vecchio*, 1929, p. 273; Planiscig, *PBI, passim*; Venturi, *Storia*, X–ii, *passim*; Middeldorf-Kriegbaum, in *Burlington Magazine*, LIII, 1928, pp. 9–17 (London figure wrongly regarded as autograph); Keutner, in *Burlington Magazine*, C, 1958, p. 428 (with correct attributions for all eight figures).
Palazzo della Signoria, Florence

VINCENZO DANTI
(b. Perugia 1530–d. Perugia 1576)

108 HONOUR VICTORIOUS OVER FALSEHOOD. Bronze
h. 35·4 cm.
Reduced copy of the large marble statue mentioned by Baldinucci 'nel cortile del palagio del Cavaliere M. Vangelista Almeni', now in the Museo Nazionale in Florence. The terracotta model for the group is in the same museum.
Bibl: Venturi, *Storia*, X–ii, p. 519 (as in silver).
Palazzo Pitti, Florence

109 LATONA AND HER CHILDREN. Light brown patination
h. 12·4 cm.
The bronze exists in an inferior version in the Victoria and Albert Museum; a variant was in the Von Hollitscher collection, and another example is in the Louvre. A widely accepted attribution to Guglielmo della Porta was first proposed by Fortnum (perhaps on the analogy of the reclining figure from the monument of Pope Paul III in the Palazzo Farnese, Rome). Bode ascribes the model to a follower of Michelangelo, and seems to have regarded it as Florentine. It is accepted as a work of Guglielmo della Porta by Planiscig. The connection with Guglielmo della Porta is remote, and the facture of the bronze is very different from that of Guglielmo della Porta's authenticated works in this medium (reliefs on the Paul III monument, plaquettes and a small bust of Pope Paul III in the Kunstgewerbe Museum, Hamburg). This and the other bronzes related to it are likely to have been made in Florence, probably from models by Vincenzo Danti, whose Venus Anadyomene in the Studiolo of the Palazzo Vecchio is recalled in the treatment of the head. The handling of the hair is related to that of the Salome in Danti's group of

the Decollation of the Baptist over the south door of the Baptistry.
Bibl: Bode, *IBS*, II, pl. CXXXVI (as follower of Michelangelo); Maclagan, in *Burlington Magazine*, XXXVI, 1920, p. 239 (as attributed to Guglielmo della Porta); Planiscig, *PBI*, p. 45, pl. CXCII (as Guglielmo della Porta). The reproductions of the Oxford and Von Hollitscher bronzes in Bode are reversed, and the Von Hollitscher bronze is mistakenly reproduced by Planiscig.
Ashmolean Museum, Oxford

110 MOSES AND THE BRAZEN SERPENT
82·2 × 172·1 cm.
Executed probably in 1560–1561 for the Grand-Duke Cosimo I, together with a bronze door for a safe, also in the Museo Nazionale, Florence.
Bibl: Catalogo, 1898, p. 395; R. Borghini, *Il Riposo*, 1584, p. 521; Venturi, *Storia*, X–ii, p. 515.
Museo Nazionale, Florence

BARTOLOMEO AMMANATI
(b. 1511–d. Florence 1582)

111 HERCULES
h. 72 cm.
This work is attributed to Ammanati, and presumably dates from the time when the artist was working in Padua for Marco Mantova Benavides.
Bibl: Moschetti, *Il Museo Civico di Padova*, 1838, p. 224.
Museo Civico, Padua

112 OMPHALE
h. 73 cm.
Pair to the preceding figure (*q.v.*).
Bibl: Moschetti, *Il Museo Civico di Padova*, 1938, p. 224.
Museo Civico, Padua

113 INKSTAND IN THE FORM OF A SATYR ON A TORTOISE. Dark patination
h. 20·5 cm.
Published by Bode as Venetian *c.* 1575, but probably made in Florence. In style the figure is closely related to the seated Fauns round the Fountain of Neptune in the Piazza della Signoria, Florence, and it is likely that the inkstand is an autograph small bronze by Ammanati, the sculptor of the fountain.
Bibl: Bode, *IBS*, III, p. 14, fig. 19.
Ashmolean Museum, Oxford

GIOVANNI BANDINI
(b. Castello 1540–d. Florence 1599)

114 JUNO
h. 96·5 cm.
From the Studiolo of Francesco de' Medici (see

No. 107). Payments for the bronze to Giovanni Bandini run from February 1572 to August 1573. The bronze is mentioned by Borghini as a work of Giovanni Bandini ('Ha il Granduca Francesco di suo una figura di bronzo fatta per Giunone').
Bibl: As for No. 107. Borghini, *Il Riposo*, 1584, p. 638; Bode, *Bronzes in the Collection of J. Pierpont Morgan*, II, 1910, No. 148 (for replica formerly in Pierpont Morgan collection); Middeldorf, in *Rivista d'Arte*, XI, 1929, p. 508.
Palazzo della Signoria, Florence

VINCENZO DE' ROSSI
(b. Fiesole 1525–d. Florence 1587)

115 VULCAN
h. 90 cm.
From the Studiolo of Francesco de' Medici (see No. 107). Payments for the bronze to Vincenzo de' Rossi run from July till September 1572. The figure is mentioned by Borghini as a work of Vincenzo de' Rossi ('Nello scrittoio del Granduca Francesco è di sua mano una statua di bronzo d'un Vulcano, che fabrica i Folgori a Giove').
Bibl: As for No. 107. Borghini, *Il Riposo*, 1584; Gramberg, in Thieme-Becker, *Künstlerlexikon*, XXIX, 1935, p. 73.
Palazzo della Signoria, Florence

GIOVANNI BOLOGNA
(b. Douai 1529–d. Florence 1608)

116 NEPTUNE   Plate 28
h. 77 cm.
The bronze is a model for the figure of Neptune on the Fountain of Neptune in Bologna. The contract for the work was signed August 20, 1563. On December 31, 1563, a master Michele of Florence, who is not otherwise known, was paid for a small wood base for a small model of Neptune which was to be presented to Pope Pius IV, together with a model of a statue of the Pope. The insistence on the qualification 'small' in this document implies that, apart from the small model to be sent to the Pope, at least one larger model was already in existence. The work was cast by Zanobi Portigiani, who subscribed to the contract in his capacity as bronze founder.
Bibl: Ducati, *Guida del Museo Civico di Bologna*, 1923, pp. 202–3; Dhanens, *Jean Boulogne*, 1956, pp. 111–22.
Museo Civico, Bologna

117 APOLLO
h. 88 cm.
From the Studiolo of Francesco de Medici (see

No. 107). Payments for the bronze to Giovanni Bologna run from December 1573 to April 1575. The model was also produced in Giovanni Bologna's workshop as a small bronze (h. 13·7 cm.); examples of these reductions exist in the Museo Nazionale, Florence, and in Berlin, Brunswick and Douai.
Bibl: As for No. 107. Dhanens, *Jean Boulogne*, 1956, pp. 182–3.
Palazzo della Signoria, Florence

118 THE DWARF MORGANTE MOUNTED ON A DRAGON
h. 36·5 cm.   Plate 29
Originally part of a fountain in the hanging garden which was installed between 1583 and 1585 on the terrace above the Loggia dei Lanzi. Payment for the bronze was made on February 4, 1584. The document recording payment establishes that the dragon was cast from a model by Cencio della Nera, the Grand-Duke's goldsmith. Before the discovery of the document the figure was attributed to Valerio Cioli.
Bibl: Bode, in *Kunst und Künstler*, IX, 1911, 632; Thieme-Becker, VII, 1912, 3–4; Planiscig, *PBI*, pl. CCXIX, fig. 373 (as Cioli); Kriegbaum, in *Münchener Jahrbuch*, III–IV, 1952–1953, p. 63; Keutner, in *Kunstgeschichtliche Studien für H. Kauffmann*, 1956, p. 240 (as Giovanni Bologna); Keutner, in *Mitteilungen des Kunsthistorischen Instituts in Florenz*, VII, 1956, p. 283 (as Giovanni Bologna); Dhanens, *Jean Boulogne*, 1956, pp. 213–14, fig. 102 (as Giovanni Bologna).
Museo Nazionale, Florence

119A ANGEL
B ANGEL
h. 50 cm., l. 75 cm. (each)
The angels form part of a series of six which, under a contract of July 24, 1579, were made for the chapel of Luca Grimaldi in S. Francesco di Castelletto in Genoa ('sex statuas aeneas Angelorum nudorum . . . super frontispicio trium tabullarum picture').The sculptures for the chapel were put in hand in Giovanni Bologna's workshop in Florence, and, according to Borghini, were still unfinished in 1584. The church and convent of S. Francesco di Castelletto were demolished after 1802, and the bronzes by Giovanni Bologna were installed in the chapel of the University before 1820.
Exh: Florence, 1940; Amsterdam, *The Triumph of Mannerism*, 1955, No. 298.
Bibl: Dhanens, *Jean Boulogne*, 1956, pp. 241–8 (with full bibliography).
The University, Genoa

120 MERCURY
h. 55·5 cm.
A first idea for the bronze in the Museo Nazionale in Naples, and perhaps for another which is said by Borghini and Vasari to have been sent to the Emperor Maximilian II of Austria, but which cannot be identified with that now in the Kunsthistorisches Museum, Vienna. Both in style and execution it is closely similar to the model for the Neptune (No. 116) and must also be dated to the end of 1563.
Exh: The Triumph of Mannerism, Rijksmuseum, Amsterdam, 1955, No. 297.
Bibl: Ducati, *Guida del Museo Civico di Bologna*, 1923, pp. 202–3; Gramberg, *Giovanni Bologna*, 1936, p. 74; Dhanens, *Jean Boulogne*, 1956, pp. 131–2.
Museo Civico, Bologna

121 MERCURY
h. 58·4 cm.
In a letter to Ottavio Farnese, Grand-Duke of Parma, of June 13, 1579, Giovanni Bologna refers to this work as having already been dispatched; there are no means of arriving at a more precise date.
Bibl: De Rinaldis, p. 375, No. 407; Filangieri di Candida, in *Napoli Nobilissima*, VI, 1897, p. 20; Dhanens, *Jean Boulogne*, 1956, pp. 125–30.
Museo Nazionale di Capodimonte, Naples

122 HERCULES AND THE ERYMANTHIAN BOAR
h. 44 cm.
In the list of groups cast in bronze from models by Giovanni Bologna, Baldinucci (ed. 1688, III, p. 136) mentions four Labours of Hercules: the Boar, the Lion, the Hydra and the Hind. The present statuette is not autograph. Other examples exist in Florence, Milan, Vienna, the Wallace collection, London, the Castiglioni collection in Vienna, and elsewhere.
Bibl: De Rinaldis, p. 383, No. 425; Dhanens, *Jean Boulogne*, 1956, p. 193.
Museo Nazionale di Capodimonte, Naples

123 CHRIST AT THE COLUMN
h. 29 cm.
The statuette, which is a superlative example of Giovanni Bologna's autograph small bronzes, exists in a second somewhat larger version in Berlin.
Bibl: Catalogo, 1898, p. 392; Bode, *IBS*, III, pl. LXXXIII; Planiscig, *PBI*, pl. 213, fig. 365; Dhanens, *Jean Boulogne*, 1956, p. 210.
Museo Nazionale, Florence

124 ARCHITECTURE. Silvered bronze
h. 36 cm.
The model depends from the large figure of Architecture which was executed in marble about 1570 and is now in the Museo Nazionale, Florence. Bronze reductions were in circulation before 1611, when one is mentioned in the collection of Markus Zeh at Augsburg. Examples are in Berlin, Boston, the Wallace Collection, the Louvre and elsewhere.
Coll: Auspitz.
Bibl: Hannema, *Catalogue of the D. G. van Beuningen Collection*, 1949, p. 168, No. 175; Dhanens, *Jean Boulogne*, 1956, pp. 162–5 (mentioning the present bronze).
D. G. van Beuningen Collection, Vierhouten

FLORENTINE (c. 1575)

125 MUSIC-MAKING PUTTI IN A SHELL. Natural dark brown patination. Traces of thin black lacquer
h. 7·7 cm.
Related by Pollak to Ferdinando Tacca's Fontana del Bacchino at Prato. The facture establishes that the bronze is Florentine.
Coll: Barsanti.
Bibl: Pollak, *Raccolta Alfredo Barsanti*, 1924, No. 68, fig. 55; Santangelo, p. 57, fig. 55.
Museo di Palazzo Venezia, Rome

Attributed to GIOVANNI CACCINI
(b. 1556–d. Florence 1612)

126 PEASANT WITH A FOWLING-LANTERN. Thin black lacquer, largely worn away
h. 25·5 cm.
The only recorded example of one of the best of the well-known series of statuettes of peasants, the production of which was begun in the workshop of Giovanni Bologna. It is related in style to the work of Giovanni Caccini and to a bronze cast from the model by Romolo Ferrucci for the destroyed Fontana del Villano in Leghorn, formerly in the A. S. Drey collection in Munich (for this see Bode, *IBS*, pl. CCXXVIII).
Coll: Barsanti.
Bibl: Pollak, *Raccolta Alfredo Barsanti*, 1924, No. 57, pl. XXVI; Santangelo, p. 54, fig. 34.
Museo di Palazzo Venezia, Rome

LODOVICO CARDI called CIGOLI
(b. Cigoli 1559–d. Rome 1613)

127 ÉCORCHÉ MALE FIGURE
h. 65 cm.
A wax model of an écorché figure made by Cigoli in 1598 exists in the Museo Nazionale, Florence. Anatomical studies of this kind, which

enjoyed great popularity in the academies,) were carried out by Cigoli under the supervision of Theodor Maierng, a Flemish teacher of anatomy in the Ospedale of S. Maria Novella. /
Bibl: Catalogo, 1898, p. 400, No. 73; Rossi, *Il Museo Nazionale di Firenze*, 1951, pp. 32, 38; *Mostra del Cigoli: Città di S. Miniato*, 1959, p. 109 (for full discussion).
Museo Nazionale, Florence

ORAZIO MOCHI
(d. 1625)

128 THE GAME OF SACCOMAZZONE. Light reddish patination
h. 31·8 cm.
Based on the model for the fountain in the Boboli Gardens, Florence, which was carved in marble by Romolo Ferrucci. Mochi's model 'in figure di due terzi di braccia incirca fù poi formato, e veggo-none tuttavia andare attorno rilievi gettati o di cera, o di gesso, o di metallo' (Baldinucci, ed. 1772, X, p. 200). The other known examples all show slight variations.
Coll: The bronze bears the mark P.C. (Corsini).
Bibl: Santangelo, p. 57, fig. 51.
Museo di Palazzo Venezia, Rome

ANTONIO SUSINI
(d. 1624)

129 HORSE KILLED BY A LION. Light reddish patination
h. 25 cm.
Reduced copy of a classical marble group in the Palazzo dei Conservatori, Rome (Helbig, *Führer*, ed. 1912, I, No. 944). It is signed: ANT. SUSI/NI OPUS/FLORE. Baldinucci (ed. 1770, VII, p. 126) includes it, and the *Bull killed by a Tiger* in the 'nota de'gruppi che si fanno di bronzo co'modelli di Gio: Bologna', and in the list of bronzes made by Giovanni Francesco Susini from models by Giovanni Bologna. A version at Detroit bears a similar signature (Valentiner, in *Burlington Magazine*, XLVI, 1925, p. 315). An example in the Liechtenstein collection forms a pair with the *Bull killed by a Tiger*.
Coll: The bronze bears the mark P.C. (Corsini).
Museo di Palazzo Venezia, Rome

130 BULL KILLED BY A LION. Light reddish patination
h. 23·4 cm.
Signed: ANT./SUSINI/F. Baldinucci mentions only the model of a *Bull killed by a Tiger* and not this group. The many replicas, which often show considerable variations, are by various artists, among them the two Susini.
Coll: The bronze bears the mark P.C. (Corsini).
Museo di Palazzo Venezia, Rome

GIOVANNI FRANCESCO SUSINI
(d. 1646)

131 DYING GLADIATOR
h. 20·3 cm.
Reduction from the antique statue in the Capitoline Museum, Rome. Signed on the rim of the shield: IO. FR. SUSINI. FLOR. FEC.
Bibl: Catalogo, 1898, p. 394; Baldinucci, ed. 1772, XII, p. 204; Thieme-Becker, XXXII, 1938, p. 305.
Museo Nazionale, Florence

132 BOAR
h. 47·6 cm.
On a wood and *pietra dura* base decorated with statuettes of Adam and Eve and two allegorical figures. Described by Baldinucci in the Reale Galleria of the Grand-Duke of Tuscany as a work executed by Susini after his stay in Rome.
Bibl: Catalogo, 1898, p. 400, No. 76; Baldinucci, ed. 1772, XII, p. 204; Thieme-Becker, XXXII, 1938, p. 305.
Museo Nazionale, Florence

133 ARES. Smooth light brown patination
h. 34 cm.
The bronze reproduces the so-called Ludovisi Ares (now in the Museo delle Terme, Rome) before its restoration by Bernini. On the rock to the left under the figure is the inscription:
IO. FR. SUSINI
FLO. FAC.
Coll: Gutekunst.
Ashmolean Museum, Oxford

PIETRO TACCA
(b. Carrara 1577–d. Florence 1640)

134A REARING HORSE
B REARING HORSE
Thin reddish Florentine patination, with some traces of black lacquer. Delicate surface working.
h. 22 and 21·3 cm. (each)
Both horses are curvetting and neighing. A similar pair, formerly in the collection of R. von Mendelsohn, Berlin, is published by Bode.
Coll: Barsanti.
Bibl: Pollak, *Raccolta Alfredo Barsanti*, 1924, Nos. 65–6, pl. XXX; Santangelo, p. 53, figs. 48–9.
Museo di Palazzo Venezia, Rome

FRANCESCO FANELLI
(Active Genoa 1609, thereafter in England 1610–1642, d. Paris 1665)

135 HORSE
h. 19·6 cm.
Presumably identical with a statuette of 'a horse ambling', described by Vertue among the bronzes by Fanelli 'bought by Wm. Duke of

Newcastle, and left at Welbeck, where the Earl of Oxford found them'.
Bibl: Vertue Note Books IV, in *Twenty-fourth Volume of the Walpole Society*, 1936, p. 110; Pope-Hennessy, in *Burlington Magazine*, XCV, 1953, pp. 157–62.
The Duke of Portland

136 ST GEORGE AND THE DRAGON. Gilt bronze
h. 19 cm. (overall 28·9 cm.)
The model exists in three forms: (i) in the collection of the Duke of Portland, on an oval base with the dragon beneath the front hooves of the horse, (ii) in the Holburne of Menstrie Museum, Bath, and (iii) in the Victoria and Albert Museum, London. The bronze was evidently very popular, and a large number of examples of the third variant are known. The present example is exceptional in that it is gilt, and that the base, decorated with gilt bronze mounts, is original.
Bibl: Pope-Hennessy, in *Burlington Magazine*, XCV, 1953, pp. 157–62 (for other versions of model); Hackenbroch, in *Connoisseur*, June 1957, pp. 9–10.
Mr Leon Bagrit, London

VENICE AND PADUA

JACOPO TATTI called SANSOVINO
(b. Florence 1486–d. Venice 1570)

137 JUPITER HOLDING A THUNDERBOLT. Black lacquer over natural brown patination   Plate 24
h. 43 cm.
The bronze is related by Planiscig to the Apollo by Sansovino on the Loggetta in the Piazza San Marco, Venice, and to the seated figures of Evangelists in St Mark's.
Bibl: Schlosser, *Werke der Kleinplastik in der Sammlung des A.H. Kaiserhauses*, I, 1910, p. 7, pl. XVIII (as Sansovino); Bode, *IBS*, III, pl. CCXXXI (as Italian, second half of the sixteenth century); Planiscig, *VB*, p. 379 (as Sansovino); Planiscig, *Bronzeplastiken*, p. 85, No. 152 (as Sansovino).
Kunsthistorisches Museum, Vienna

138 CHRIST IN LIMBO. Traces of gilding under a thick, dark brown varnish. The cross cast separately
h. 40·6 cm.   Plate 23
This work, which forms part of the Este collection, is identical with 'Un Christo che tiene una croce, con piedistallo nero', mentioned in 1684 among the bronze or metal statues, 'molte delle quali erano a Sassuolo', in the *Inventario delle statue ecc. che sono al presente nel casino di S.A. Serma. fuori di Porta Castello*. In style it is associable with the tabernacle door executed by Sansovino for St Mark's, Venice.
Bibl: Planiscig, *Die Estensische Kunstsammlung*, I, 1919, No. 191; Modigliani, *Catalogo degli oggetti d'arte e storia restituiti dall' Austria-Ungheria ed esposti nel R. Palazzo Venezia in Roma*, 1923, p. 65, No. 2.
Museo Estense, Modena

DANESE CATTANEO
(b. Carrara 1509–d. Padua 1573)

139 BUST OF LAZZARO BONAMICO   Plate 26
The bust was executed for the tomb of Bonamico in S. Giovanni di Verdara, Padua. After the suppression of this church it passed into the hands of G. B. Roberti, by whose nephew it was presented to the Museo Civico at Bassano. Bonamico, who was lecturer in Latin and Greek in the University at Padua, died on February 11, 1552.
Bibl: Roberti, in *Arte e Storia*, 1886, p. 45; Planiscig, *VB*, p. 424, fig. 445; Venturi, *Storia*, X–iii, p. 12.
Museo Civico, Bassano

140 LUNA. Brown natural patination with dark brown varnish
h. 51 cm.
The attribution to Cattaneo is due to Planiscig, who suggests that the bronze was possibly cast from a model made by this sculptor for a statue of the Moon (as goddess of Silver) designed as a counterpart to a statue of Apollo (as god of Gold) on a fountain in the courtyard of the Zecca in Venice. According to Vasari, the scheme was to include a third figure representing Copper ('per lo rame'), but only the Apollo was executed. The Apollo is now in the courtyard of Ca Pesaro.
Bibl: Schlosser, *Werke der Kleinplastik in der Skulpturensammlung des A.H. Kaiserhauses*, I, 1910, p. 12 (unidentified Florentine sculptor *c.* 1550); Bode, *IBS*, III, pl. CCXXXI (Italian second half of sixteenth century); Planiscig, *VB*, p. 421 (for Zecca fountain); Planiscig, *Bronzeplastiken*,

pp. 93–4 (as Cattaneo).
Kunsthistorisches Museum, Vienna

141 MARINE VENUS
h. 50·3 cm.
Attributed to Danese Cattaneo, along with a Marine Venus, also standing on a globe, and an allegorical figure of the Moon (No. 140) both in the Kunsthistorisches Museum, Vienna.
Bibl: Catalogo, 1898, p. 82, No. 221; Planiscig, *VB*, pp. 411 ff.; Planiscig, *PBI*, p. 34, pl. CLI.
Museo Nazionale, Florence

142 THE FEAST OF THE GODS. Black lacquer much rubbed. Head of female figure on right broken and replaced
h. 34 cm.
The composition is known through two variants of the present relief in the Cleveland Museum of Art (formerly Delmar collection, Budapest) and the Metropolitan Museum of Art, New York (formerly Rosenfeld collection). There are a number of differences (e.g. in the sea-food on the table and the figures in the left background) between the three versions. The casting is of higher quality in this than in the two American examples, and it is likely that the present relief and the relief in New York (in which a head is also broken) precede the Cleveland relief, which is more highly worked. The subject has been variously explained as (i) Danese Cattaneo as the adopted son of Venice feasted by Neptune and protected by Apollo from the assaults of Mars (Planiscig), (ii) the apotheosis of Sebastiano Venier (Phillips), (iii) the Nuptials of Peleus and Thetis (Delmar).
Coll: Marchioness of Crewe.
Bibl: Planiscig, in *WJ*, n.f. x, 1936, pp. 131–6; Phillips, in *Bulletin of the Metropolitan Museum of Art*, XXXIV, 1939, pp. 192–6; Delmar, in *Gazette des Beaux-Arts*, n.s., XXVII, 1945, pp. 347–56.
Victoria and Albert Museum, London

TIZIANO MINIO
(b. Padua *c.* 1517–d. Padua 1552)

143 NEPTUNE. Dark patination partly rubbed; both eyes bored
h. 29·7 cm.
In its complete form the model shows Neptune standing on a base in the form of a chariot drawn by two sea-horses. Versions of the complete model are recorded in the Beit collection and at Brunswick. In a version of the complete model formerly in the collection of Sir George Leon the breasts of the Neptune and the mouths of the sea-horses are bored and fitted with small tubes

as a table-fountain. Two versions of the Neptune alone are in the Kunsthistorisches Museum, Vienna. The attribution to Tiziano Minio (proposed initially by Planiscig) is more plausible than an attribution to Jacopo Sansovino (proposed by Bode and later followed by Planiscig).
Coll: Cassell, Eckstein.
Bibl: Bode, *Catalogue of the Collection of Pictures and Bronzes in the Possession of Mr Otto Beit*, 1913, p. 62, for Beit version ('closely connected with the later art of Sansovino . . . may indeed be by his own hand'); Planiscig, *VB*, p. 406, fig. 429 (Beit version as Tiziano Minio); Planiscig, *Bronzeplastiken*, p. 86 (Vienna versions as Sansovino).
Victoria and Albert Museum, London

144 FIGURATED BASE
h. 10 cm.
Attributed work. In the types and execution it is in conformity with the Bearded Nude by Tiziano Minio in the Kunsthistorisches Museum, Vienna, and with the Saints Peter and Paul formerly in the Estensische Kunstsammlung, Vienna.
Coll: Carrand.
Bibl: Planiscig, *VB*, pp. 404–5, fig. 431; *PBI*, pl. CXLVI, fig. 256.
Museo Nazionale, Florence

ALFONSO ALBERGHETTI
(Ferrarese, active in Venice 1559–1585)

145 VASE
h. 23·2 cm.
Bears the artist's signature and the date 1562. Alberghetti is known as the author of one of the well-heads in the cortile of the Palazzo Ducale in Venice, which was cast in 1559.
Bibl: Rossi, in Thieme-Becker, *s.v.*
Museo Artistico-Industriale, Palazzo Barberini, Rome

ALESSANDRO VITTORIA
(b. Trent 1525–d. Venice 1608)

146 BUST OF TOMMASO RANGONE
Originally in S. Geminiano, Venice, in a passage leading to the sacristy. Later transferred to the Sala Superiore of the Ateneo. During this move the bust lost a marble dedicatory inscription, recorded by Cicogna (*Delle iscriz. Venez.*, IV, Venezia, 1834, 101): RELIGIONI VIRTUTI/THOMAS PHILOLOG RANG RAVEN/PHYS EQ COM M B PAL ECCL/ET FAB PROCURATOR. Rangone received permission to install the bust and memorial tablet in S. Geminiano in 1571. The terracotta model is in the Museo Correr, Venice.
Bibl: Planiscig, *VB*, p. 483; Venturi, *Storia*, X–iii, p. 156.
Ateneo Veneto, Venice

147 NEPTUNE. Reddish-brown patination   Plate 25
 h. 49·5 cm.
One of the finest of Vittoria's surviving bronzes, the Neptune is related in handling to the bronze St John the Baptist in S. Francesco della Vigna, Venice. The S. Francesco della Vigna Baptist is dated by Cessi *c.* 1562, but is rightly assigned by Planiscig to a considerably later date. Both bronzes were perhaps made *c.* 1580–1585. The subject of the bronze is Neptune stilling the waves to protect the Trojan fleet (*Aeneid*, I, 135).
Coll: Salting.
Bibl: Bode, *IBS*, II, p. 23, pl. CLVII (as Alessandro Vittoria?); Planiscig, *VB*, p. 477 (as Vittoria); Planiscig, *PBI*, pl. CLIV (as Vittoria); Cessi, *Alessandro Vittoria bronzista*, 1960, pp. 42–4 (as Vittoria).
Victoria and Albert Museum, London

148 ALLEGORY OF WINTER. Black lacquer over dark brown natural patination
 h. 33 cm.
The attribution to Vittoria of this impressive bronze is due to Planiscig. A replica of rather lower quality exists in the Museo Estense, Modena.
Bibl: Schlosser, *Werke der Kleinplastik in der Skulpturensammlung des A.H. Kaiserhauses*, I, 1910, p. 9 (certainly Tuscan, by a Florentine imitator of Michelangelo); Bode, *IBS*, III, pl. CCXXV (Florentine follower of Michelangelo); Planiscig, *VB*, p. 475 (as Vittoria); Planiscig, *Bronzeplastiken*, pp. 102–3 (as Vittoria); Cessi, *Alessandro Vittoria bronzista*, 1960, p. 45 (as Vittoria).
Kunsthistorisches Museum, Vienna

149 MILO OF CROTON
 h. 31 cm.
Originally in the Mantova Benavides collection at Padua, later in S. Giovanni di Verdara, Padua, subsequently in the Museo Archeologico, Venice. In the catalogue of Andrea Mantova Benavides, it is described as the work of an 'egregio scultore'. The attribution to Vittoria is due to Fogolari.
Bibl: Bode, *IBS*, pl. CXXXV (as by a Florentine artist under the influence of Michelangelo); Fogolari, in *Bollettino d'Arte*, ser. ii, VI, 1926–1927, p. 382 (as Vittoria); Cessi, *Alessandro Vittoria bronzista*, 1960, pp. 40–1 (as Vittoria).
Ca d'Oro, Venice

150 NEGRESS. Light brown natural patina and traces of brown lacquer
 h. 32·5 cm.
Versions of the model, known as the 'Negro Venus', exist in the Louvre, the Museum at Brunswick, the Grünes Gewölbe, Dresden, the Metropolitan Museum, New York, and elsewhere. The attribution to Vittoria, which is due to Planiscig, has been repeatedly contested. The style of the bronze is not, however, consistent with the Tuscan origin which has often been proposed for it. The object held in the right hand is the handle of a mirror, and the subject is perhaps an allegory of Vanity.
Bibl: Schlosser, *Werke der Kleinplastik in der Skulpturensammlung des A.H. Kaiserhauses*, I, 1910, p. 12 (as Florentine sixteenth century, unidentified artist of the generation preceding Giovanni Bologna's); Planiscig, *VB*, pp. 494–6 (as Vittoria); Planiscig, *Bronzeplastiken*, 103 (as Vittoria); Landais, *Les Bronzes italiens de la Renaissance*, 1958, p. 116 (as Florentine, *c.* 1570–1575); Cessi, *Alessandro Vittoria bronzista*, 1960, p. 57 (Tuscan sculptor of the second half of the sixteenth century close to Danese Cattaneo).
Kunsthistorisches Museum, Vienna

151 NEPTUNE. Gilt bronze
 h. 15·5 cm.
The bronze is related in reverse to a small bronze Neptune of much inferior quality from the Vittoria workshop in the Museo Civico at Padua. A trident was presumably held in the raised left hand.
Bibl: Cessi, *Alessandro Vittoria bronzista*, 1960, pl. 6 (for bronze at Padua).
Mr Paul Wallraf, London

152 VULCAN. Gilt bronze
 h. 16 cm.
The model, which seems to date from the same time as the Milo of Croton (No. 149), is unrecorded.
Mr Paul Wallraf, London

153 JUNO
A superior version of the model in the Lederer collection, Vienna, is published by Planiscig. The bronze was produced in some numbers as the top of a firedog, where it had as its counterpart a Jupiter, and most of the surviving examples are coarse in quality. The present example is not autograph. The model is, however, an important document in so far as it offers evidence of Vittoria's debt to Parmegianino.
Bibl: Planiscig, *VB*, pp. 492–3 (for Lederer bronze); Cessi, *Alessandro Vittoria bronzista*, 1960, p. 56.
Museo Civico, Padua

154 LAMP IN THE FORM OF A WOMAN WARMING HER
HANDS AT A BRAZIER
h. 20 cm.
Mistakenly reproduced by Bode, along with the
Vittoria *Winter* in Vienna (No. 148), as the work
of a Florentine imitator of Michelangelo. A
related bronze of a bearded man warming his
hands is in the Victoria and Albert Museum.
Bibl: Bode, *IBS*, III, pl. CCXXV.
Museo Nazionale di Capodimonte, Naples

155 ST PETER. Silver, parcel gilt
h. 54·5 cm.
In the open book are the words: TIBI DABO
CLAVES/REGNI CELORV.
Coll: Nunez; Auspitz.
Bibl: Hannema, *Catalogue of the D. G. van
Beuningen Collection*, 1949, p. 195, No. 207 (as a
Patriarch by Vittoria).
Museum Boymans-van Beuningen, Rotterdam

156 ST PAUL. Silver, parcel gilt
h. 52·5 cm.
In the open book are the words: ACCIPITE
GLADIVM SPIRITVS/QVOD EST VEREVM DEI. See
No. 155.
Coll: Nunez; Auspitz.
Bibl: Hannema, *Catalogue of the D. G. van
Beuningen Collection*, 1949, p. 195, No. 208 (as a
Patriarch by Vittoria).
Museum Boymans-van Beuningen, Rotterdam

MASTER OF THE HAGGARD OLD MEN
(Probably active Venice c. 1560–1580)

157 RIVER GOD. Golden brown patination. Cast in
one with its rectangular base
h. 24·1 cm.
The statuette forms part of a group of bronzes
of ascetic bearded men by a single hand, apparently associable with Vittoria. The reintegration
of the group is due to Planiscig.
Bibl: Schlosser, *Werke der Kleinplastik in der
Skulpturensammlung des A.H. Kaiserhauses*, I, 1910,
p. 17 (without attribution); Planiscig, *VB*,
pp. 471–3 (as Meister der Hageren Eltern);
Planiscig, *Bronzeplastiken*, pp. 106–7 (as Meister
der Hageren Eltern).
Kunsthistorisches Museum, Vienna

GIULIO DEL MORO
(b. Verona 1555–active Venice till 1614)

158 THE REDEEMER. Dense black lacquer. Solid cast
h. 47·5 cm.
The bronze is attributed to Giulio del Moro. It
may be compared with the Redeemer in S. Maria
del Giglio, Venice, and with the signed figure of
the Redeemer by Giulio del Moro on the Dolfin
Monument in S. Salvatore.
Coll: Barsanti.
Bibl: Pollak, *Raccolta Alfredo Barsanti*, 1924,
No. 80, pl. XXXV; Santangelo, p. 44, fig. 47.
Museo di Palazzo Venezia, Rome

GIROLAMO CAMPAGNA
(b. Venice 1552?–d. Venice 1623?)

159 KNEELING YOUTH CARRYING A SHELL. Gilt bronze,
partly rubbed
h. 20·5 cm.
The bronze, which was evidently planned as a
salt-cellar, exists in a number of versions. Other
examples are in the Ashmolean Museum, Oxford,
and the Kunsthistorisches Museum, Vienna.
Coll: Salting.
Bibl: Bode, *IBS*, II, p. 24, pl. CLXII (Oxford
version as Venetian c. 1575); Planiscig, *VB*,
p. 543 (Von Frey version as Campagna); Planiscig, *PBI*, pl. CLXIX (Vienna version as Campagna).
Victoria and Albert Museum, London

160A MELEAGER
B ATALANTA
Smooth black lacquer, light natural patination
showing through on the back.
h. 53 cm. (each)
From a pair of fire-dogs. Other examples of the
Meleager are in the Museo Correr, Venice, and,
with slight variations, in the Victoria and Albert
Museum, London; a version of the Atalanta is
in the Museo del Castello Sforzesco, Milan.
Coll: Barsanti.
Bibl: Pollak, *Raccolta Alfredo Barsanti*, 1924,
Nos. 89–90, pl. XLI; Santangelo, p. 45, figs. 42,
43.
Museo di Palazzo Venezia, Rome

GIUSEPPE DE LEVI
(Active Verona, late sixteenth century)

161 INKSTAND WITH CHRIST AND THE WOMAN OF
SAMARIA. Dark patination
h. 16·5 cm., w. 21 cm.
The bronze, which is unrecorded and does not
exist in any other version, is inscribed beneath the
base:

IOSEPH
DE.LEVIS
.VER.
.F.

Mr Leon Bagrit, London

A. E. LEVIS
(Active in Verona in 1594)

162 DOOR-KNOCKER
h. 29·8 cm.
The knocker, which does not exist in any other version, is signed A. E. LEVVIS. 94. This artist (who is otherwise unrecorded) was presumably a kinsman of Giuseppe de Levi (see above).
Bibl: Planiscig, in manuscript catalogue of the Auriti collection.
H.E. Giacinto Auriti, Rome

TIZIANO ASPETTI
(b. Padua 1565–d. Pisa 1607)

163 MARS. Rich dark brown patination
h. 59 cm.
The bronze is known through a second version of equivalent quality in the Frick collection, New York (formerly Pierpont Morgan collection). The bases are identical save for certain unimportant details, but the two figures are set differently on their plinths and the helmet of that in New York is completed by a plume. It has been suggested that in view of the gorgon head on the shield, Perseus and not Mars is represented; the present figure is, however, accompanied by a Venus (No. 164), and this explanation of the subject must therefore be incorrect. Versions of the bronze without the base are also known (former Kauffmann collection, Berlin, and elsewhere).
Coll: Leon.
Bibl: Planiscig, *VB*, pp. 568–9 (Frick version as Aspetti); Venturi, *Storia*, X-iii, 1937, pp. 306, 310–11 (Frick version as Aspetti); Maclagan, in *The Frick Collection*, VI, p. 12, No. 44 (Frick version as Aspetti).
Mr Peter Harris, London

164 VENUS. Rich dark brown patination
h. 59 cm.
Companion piece to No. 163.
Coll: Leon.
Mr Peter Harris, London

165 FAITH. Natural patination with traces of black lacquer
h. 47 cm.
A reduced version of one of the four statuettes of the Cardinal Virtues executed for the altar of the chapel of St Anthony in S. Antonio at Padua. Removed in 1651, they were later placed on the balustrade of the high altar of the church. The models were presented for inspection and approved on October 25, 1593, and the contract was drawn up on November 6.
H.E. Giacinto Auriti, Rome

166 MARINE VENUS
h. 43·5 cm.
Top of a fire-dog. In a very similar bronze reproduced by Planiscig as in the Read collection, London, the hair and the dolphin are differently treated.
Bibl: Moschetti, *Il Museo Civico di Padova*, 1938, p. 223; Planiscig, *VB*, pp. 581–3.
Museo Civico, Padua

CAMILLO MARIANI
(b. Vicenza 1556–d. Rome 1611)

167 SAN CRESCENTINO AND THE DRAGON
h. 83 cm.
Initially ascribed by Calzini to Donnino Ambrosi, it was recognized as a work of Mariani by Fiocco, who dated it about 1595, in which year Vincenzo Scamozzi wrote to Francesco Maria della Rovere, Duke of Urbino, recommending Mariani as a youth of great promise for the future of sculpture (Gronau, *Documenti artistici urbinati*, 1935, pp. 39–40, 271). The bronze stood on a column in the square in front of the Palazzo del Comune at Urbino.
Exh: Rome, 1886.
Bibl: Esposizione del 1886, Rome, Museo Artistico-Industriale, p. 19, No. 10; Calzini, *Urbino e i suoi monumenti*, 1897, pp. 94–5 (as Ambrosi); Fiocco, in *Le Arti*, III, 1940–1, p. 80 (as Mariani).
Municipio, Urbino

NICCOLO ROCCATAGLIATA
(Active in Venice before 1593–d. Genoa after 1636)

168 THE EXPULSION FROM PARADISE. Light brown natural patina with traces of dark lacquer
h. 23·8 cm.
The Adam exists as an independent statuette, also in the Kunsthistorisches Museum, where it is accompanied by a figure of Eve differently posed. The single figures are regarded by Planiscig as derivatives from the present group, of which a replica exists in the Museo Civico at Belluno. The attribution of the bronzes to Roccatagliata is due to Schlosser, who draws attention to their relationship to Tintoretto.
Bibl: Bode, *IBS*, II, pl. CLX (as Venetian *c.* 1570); Schlosser, *Werke der Kleinplastik in der Skulpturensammlung des A.H. Kaiserhauses*, I, 1910, p. 8 (as Roccatagliata); Planiscig, *VB*, p. 619 (as Roccatagliata); Planiscig, *Bronzeplastiken*, pp. 120–1 (as Roccatagliata).
Kunsthistorisches Museum, Vienna

169 BACCHUS. Dense black patination. Cup broken from foot   Plate 27
h. 43·5 cm.
A second version of the model, of equivalent quality, in which the figure is accompanied by a Satyr, is in the Hermitage at Leningrad. The model was also used in a reduced form in the Roccatagliata studio as a decoration for fire-dogs. The pose, as is not unusual with Roccatagliata, recalls works by Tintoretto.
Coll: Salting.
Victoria and Albert Museum, London

170 ST GEORGE
h. 18 cm.
An early work which may be compared with the bronzes cast for S. Giorgio Maggiore, Venice, in 1593.
Coll: Franchetti.
Ca d'Oro, Venice

171 FOUR MUSIC-MAKING PUTTI. Gilt bronze
h. 18 cm., w. (of bases) 7 cm.
The four figures are related to the celebrated music-making putti by Roccatagliata in the Estensische Kunstsammlung at Vienna.
Bibl: Sutton, in *Connoisseur*, June 1961, p. 7.
Mr Paul Wallraf, London

172 PLAYING PUTTI
h. 25 cm.
A late work, related to the altar frontal signed by Roccatagliata and his son Sebastiano and dated 1633, in the sacristy of S. Moisè in Venice.
Bibl: Planiscig, *PBI*, pl. CLXXX, fig. 311.
Museo Correr, Venice

173 ANGEL. Smooth black lacquer
h. 19·3 cm.
A pair to the figure was formerly in the Pollak collection.
Coll: Barsanti.
Bibl: Pollak, *Raccolta Alfredo Barsanti*, 1924, No. 103, pl. XLVII; Santangelo, 49, fig. 28.
Museo di Palazzo Venezia, Rome

VENETIAN (middle of the sixteenth century)

174 ATLAS. Black lacquer, highly polished
h. 23 cm.
Related to the Atlas in the Palazzo Ducale in Venice, which is regarded by Venturi as an early work by Tiziano Aspetti, but is certainly of earlier date. The present bronze is also to be dated about 1540–1550.
Coll: Barsanti.
Bibl: Pollak, *Raccolta Alfredo Barsanti*, Rome, 1924, No. 81, pl. XXXVI; Santangelo, p. 38, fig. 39.
Museo di Palazzo Venezia, Rome

175 MALE NUDE ON HORSEBACK. Solid cast. Right leg of rider and right foreleg of horse broken and missing. Dark patina
h. 26·2 cm.
Ascribed to Rustici. A second version of the bronze was in the Pierpont Morgan collection; in this the riding figure is closely similar in pose, but the head of the horse is turned outwards to the right. Copies in silver by German artists are also known (for these see *The Triumph of Mannerism*, Amsterdam, 1955, No. 428). The model is difficult to reconcile with Rustici's authenticated works, and can hardly date from earlier than the middle of the sixteenth century.
Coll: Private collection, Berlin. Acquired by the Rijksmuseum in 1924.
Exh: Decorative Arts of the Italian Renaissance, 1400–1600, Detroit, Institute of Art, 1958–1959, No. 252 (as Rustici).
Bibl: Bode, *Bronzes in the Collection of J. Pierpont Morgan*, I, 1910, pp. xxv, 28, pl. LXVII (Morgan bronze as Paduan, late sixteenth century); Schottmüller, in *Art in America*, XIII, 1925, p. 63, fig. 2 (Rijksmuseum bronze as Tiziano Aspetti).
Rijksmuseum, Amsterdam

176 CANDLESTICK. Smooth black patination
h. 34 cm.
Coll: Barsanti.
Bibl: Pollak, *Raccolta Alfredo Barsanti*, 1924, No. 43, pl. XLVI; Santangelo, p. 34, pl. 61.
Museo di Palazzo Venezia, Rome

177 PUTTO
h. 23·5 cm.
The bronze is regarded by Nicodemi as Paduan, late fifteenth century, and by Peroni as Venetian, second half of the sixteenth century. The latter view is the more convincing.
Bibl: Rizzini, p. 9, No. 23; Nicodemi, in *Dedalo*, I, 1920, 221, p. 464; Peroni, in *Arte Veneta*, XIII–XIV, 1959–1960, p. 104.
Musei Civici, Brescia

VENETIAN (c. 1575)

178 THE THREE GRACES
h. 17 cm.
Attributed by Planiscig to Girolamo Campagna.
Bibl: Bode, *IBS*, II, pl. CLXI (as an anonymous Venetian sculptor c. 1570); Planiscig, *PBI*, pl. CLXVII, fig. 289 (as Campagna); Hacken-

broch, in *Connoisseur*, CXLIII, p. 216 (version in Bagrit collection as Campagna).
Museo Estense, Modena

179 SALT-CELLAR IN THE FORM OF A SHELL
h. 15 cm.
Not by Riccio, as was supposed by Bode, but by a late sixteenth-century Venetian artist of the *terra ferma* influenced by Vittoria.
Bibl: Ricci, *Il Palazzo Pubblico di Siena e la Mostra di Antica Arte Senese*, 1904, p. 57, fig. 148; Bode, *IBS*, I, pl. XLVIII (as Riccio).
Museo Civico, Siena

180 VENUS CHASTISING CUPID. Natural yellowish patination with thin black lacquer
h. 20 cm.
Another version with slight variations was formerly in the Figdor collection, Vienna. The facture of both bronzes resembles that of the *Three Graces* in the Museo Estense in Modena (No. 178), which is attributed to Girolamo Campagna by Planiscig, and more convincingly by Bode to an unidentified Venetian artist active about 1570. For the origin and evolution of the subject in art and literature see E. Tietze-Conrat,

Die Bronzen der fürstlich Liechtensteinschen Kunstkammer, 1918, pp. 11 f.
Coll: Barsanti.
Bibl: Pollak, *Raccolta Alfredo Barsanti*, 1924, No. 73, pl. 32; Santangelo, p. 55, fig. 36.
Museo di Palazzo Venezia, Rome

PADUAN (second half of the sixteenth century)

181 HERCULES RESTING. Gilt bronze. Perhaps a furniture mount
h. 21 cm.
The pair to the present figure exists in two examples in the Museo Correr, Venice, which are identical even to the base, with versions in the Auriti collection, Rome, and the Bayerisches Nationalmuseum, Munich. Hercules has his hand on a ladder, crowned with the Doge's *Corno*, the emblem of the Gradenigo. The bronze is perhaps by an unknown artist related to Giovanni Gavino active in the circle of Marco Mantova Benavides.
Bibl: Moschetti, *Il Museo Civico di Padova*, 1938, p. 224, fig. 104; Planiscig, in *PJ*, LIII, 1932, p. 16 (as Venetian, seventeenth century); Weihrauch, Bayerisches Nationalmuseum, Munich, *Die Bildwerke in Bronze*, p. 112, No. 137 (as Venetian, seventeenth century).
Museo Civico, Padua

LOMBARDY

LEONE LEONI
(b. Arezzo *c.* 1509–d. Milan 1590)

182 AN ARMED WARRIOR
h. 8·5 cm.
A small handle for a vase, perfume-burner or bell. The figure is usually identified as Mars. The attribution to Leone Leoni due to Planiscig.
Bibl: Bode, *IBS*, II, p. 18, pl. CXXXVI (as follower of Michelangelo); Planiscig, *PBI*, pl. CXCVII, fig. 341 (as Leoni).
Museo Estense, Modena

183 BOWL
h. 20 cm.
The exuberant ornamentation with figures, plant motifs and animals is not easy to reconcile with the crisp and free style of Leone Leoni, to whom the bronze has been attributed.

Bibl: Planiscig, *PBI*, pl. CXCVII, fig. 342 (as Leoni).
Museo del Castello Sforzesco, Milan

LOMBARD (?) (*c.* 1575)

184 STANDING WARRIOR
h. 28·3 cm.
Venturi has emphasized the spontaneity of the Michelangelesque elements in this extremely delicate bronze, which recalls the work of Guglielmo della Porta. In style, type and armour it resembles the Vienna Prisoner, attributed by Planiscig to Leone Leoni (*Bronzeplastiken*, p. 130, No. 226).
Bibl: Venturi, *La Galleria Estense in Modena*, 1882, p. 100; Bode, *IBS*, II, pl. CXXXVIII.
Museo Estense, Modena

BASTIANO TORRIGIANI
(Bologna, active in Rome 1573–1596)

185 POPE GREGORY XIV (Pope, 1590–1591). On the cartouche is the inscription GRE. XIV. Brown patina
h. 31·5 cm.
Bode attributed this small bust to the same hand as two large papal busts in the Kaiser Friedrich Museum, Berlin, which are by Torrigiani. The name of Taddeo Landini is proposed by Schlosser. Other examples are in Schloss Friedrichskron, the Gewerbe Museum at Reichenberg, and at the former Pierpont Morgan collection.
Coll: Mylius, Genoa; Empress Frederick, Kronberg; Mannheimer, Amsterdam. Acquired in 1952.
Bibl: Die Kunstsammlungen Ihrer Majestät der Kaiserin und Köningin Friedrich im Schloss Friedrichshof, 1896, pp. 17–18; Bode, in *PJ,* IV, 1883, p. 145; Bode, *IBS,* III, pp. 14–15, fig. 18; Bode,

Bronzes in the Collection of J. Pierpont Morgan, New York, II, No. 125; Bode, *Bildwerke des Kaiser-Friedrich-Museums, Die Italienische Bildwerke der Renaissance und des Barocks,* 1930, No. 6. *Rijksmuseum, Amsterdam*

NICCOLO CORDIERI
(b. Lorraine 1567–d. Rome 1612)

186 CHARITY. Dense black patination
h. 37 cm.
The statuette corresponds with the group of Charity by Cordieri on the monument of Luisa Deti Aldobrandini, mother of Pope Clement VIII, in S. Maria sopra Minerva, Rome (1592–1605).
Coll: Salting.
Bibl: Bode, *IBS,* II, p. 19, pl. CXLII (as Michelangelesque); Planiscig, *PBI,* pl. CLXIII, fig. 283 (as Venetian, second half of sixteenth century). *Victoria and Albert Museum, London*

MID-SEVENTEENTH AND EIGHTEENTH CENTURIES

◆

ROME

GIAN LORENZO BERNINI
(b. Naples 1598–d. Rome 1680)

187A–D FOUR GROTESQUE MASKS
Bronze, fire gilt, fitted in the interior for use as finials on some larger complex. The four heads vary both in the casting and chiselling
h. 15 cm.
The four masks recall the Damned Soul in the Palazzo di Spagna in Rome in their open mouths and their distorted features; the latter recall the best and most elaborate of Bernini's caricatures. According to a tradition handed down in Bernini's family, they would have decorated the carriage in which Pope Innocent X attended the inauguration of the Fountain of the Four Rivers in the Piazza Navona. It is likely, however, that they are identical with 'quattro testine di gettiti in bronzo con li suoi piedi di pietra, quali erano li nasi della carrozza del Cavaliers', cited in the

1706 inventory of the contents of the residence of Bernini's heirs, and that they therefore decorated Bernini's carriage. The four heads are not visible on the carriage shown in the engraving by Louis Rouhier of the Piazza Navona on June 12, 1651.
Eredi Bernini, Rome

ALESSANDRO ALGARDI
(b. Bologna 1595–d. Rome 1654)

188 POPE INNOCENT X (Pope 1644–1655). Bronze and porphyry
This magnificent bust, in which the porphyry is carved with unparalleled freedom, is the finest, and in all probability the latest, of Algardi's portrait busts of Pope Innocent X. The treatment of the head is related to that in the commemorative statue of the Pope by Algardi in the Palazzo dei Conservatori.

Bibl: Fraschetti, *Il Bernini*, 1900, p. 211 (as 'opera discreta di un allievo del Bernini'); Barton, *A Preliminary Study of Alessandro Algardi*, Harvard Ph.D. thesis, 1952, p. 202 (as Algardi); Wittkower, *Bernini*, 1955, p. 212 (as Algardi, after 1650).
Palazzo Doria, Rome

189 ST MICHAEL OVERCOMING SATAN
h. 74 cm.
Stated by Bellori to have been made by Algardi for the sacristy of S. Michele in Bosco, Bologna, on the commission of Abbate Taddeo Pepoli. Between 1666, when it is mentioned by Masini as being in the Sacristy, and 1686, when it was described by Malvasia, it was moved to the library of the convent. A passage in a manuscript of Baldinucci (Florence, Bibl. Nazionale, *Cod. Magliabecchiano*, II, 11, 110, p. 54) records that the group was cast from Algardi's model by Domenico Guidi (1628–1701), who was also responsible for the casting of Algardi's Allegory of Earth at Aranjuez. As pointed out by Hess, this information necessitates a dating after 1647, and is not consistent with the early dating proposed by Hermanin.
Bibl: Bellori, *Le Vite de' pittori, scultori et architetti moderni, Parte prima*, 1672, p. 392; Masini, *Bologna perlustrata*, 1666, p. 127; Malvasia, *Pitture Scolture et Architetture . . . della Citta di Bologna*, 1792, p. 427; Ricci Zucchini, *Guida di Bologna*, ed. 1930, p. 26; Muñoz, in *Atti e memorie della R. Accademia di S. Luca: Annuario, 1912*, II, 1913, pp. 55–6; Hermanin, in *Belvedere*, V, 1924, p. 58; Hess, in *Münchner Jahrbuch der bildenden Kunst*, n.f., VIII, 1931, pp. 300–2; Hess, *Die Künstlerbiographien von Giovanni Battista Passeri*, 1934, p. 196n.
Museo Civico, Bologna

190 CHARITY. Dark brown patination
h. 47·6 cm.
The model, which has not been published, is by the same hand as a Virgin and Child of which versions in the Ehem. Staatliche Museen, Berlin, and the Rhode Island School of Design are ascribed to Ercole Ferrata. Decisive arguments against the attribution to Ferrata are advanced, in the case of a version of the Virgin and Child in the Palazzo Ducale at Urbino, by Wittkower, who ascribes it to Algardi.

Bibl: Wittkower, in *Rassegna Marchigiana*, VII, 1928, pp. 41–4 (Urbino bronze as Algardi).
Victoria and Albert Museum, London

MELCHIORE CAFFÀ
(b. Malta probably 1635–d. Rome before 1668)

191 THE BAPTISM OF CHRIST
h. 45 cm.
The marble group of the Baptism of Christ for the high altar of the Cathedral at Valletta, Malta, was carried out by Giuseppe Mazzuoli after the death of Caffà from a model by this sculptor. Baldinucci records that late in the seventeenth century reductions of the group were to be seen in the fonderia of St Peter's ('e fino a quest'anno veggonsi gli stessi modelli nella fonderia di S. Pietro'). A terracotta sketch-model, apparently made in connection with the bronze reductions and not with the marble, is in the Biblioteca Vaticana. Examples in bronze are at Pirano, Rome (Galleria Corsini), Copenhagen and elsewhere.
Coll: Auspitz.
Bibl: Morpurgo, in *Dedalo*, IV, 1924, p. 456 (for Pirano bronze as Bernini); Ozzola, in *Dedalo*, VII, 1926–1927, p. 135; Wittkower, in *Zeitschrift für Bildende Kunst*, LXII, 1928–1929, pp. 227–31 (full analysis); Hannema, *Catalogue of the D. G. van Beuningen Collection*, 1949, p. 171, No. 180.
D. G. van Beuningen Collection, Vierhouten

ROMAN (?) (c. 1700)

192 HERCULES BRINGING CERBERUS TO EURYSTHEUS.
Smooth brown patination
h. 34·5 cm.
The model, which is unpublished, belongs to a series of the Labour of Hercules of which three other groups are in the Untermyer collection, New York. The Untermyer bronzes represent Hercules and the Serpents, Hercules and the Nemean Lion, and Hercules with the Erymanthian Boar. The bases of all four are uniform. There is some difficulty in localizing and dating the groups, which seem, from the form of the cradle in the first of the Untermyer bronzes, to date from about 1700. A Roman origin is conjectural, and is based on analogies with painting; there are no seventeenth-century Roman bronzes that are closely comparable.
Mr Brinsley Ford, London

MASSIMILIANO SOLDANI
(b. Florence 1658–d. Montevarchi 1740)

193 SPRING. Dark brown patination
h. 47 cm., w. 66 cm.
Signed: MAXIMILIANIS SOLDANI-BENZI NOBILIS FLORENTINVS FAC. ANNO. 1715
At the right the goddess Flora is enthroned, supported by Vertumnus and Pomona. At the left nymphs are decorating a herm. A version of the relief in the Bayerisches National Museum, Munich (see No. 196 below), is dated 1711 and has on a cartouche on the frame the inscription: VERE . NOVO . OMNIGENIS . SOLA . FETIBUS . IMPLEAT . DETQVE . NOVM . COELI . VIS . GENITIVA . JUBAR.
H.M. The Queen

194 SUMMER. Dark brown patination
h. 47 cm., w. 66 cm.
Signed: MAXIMILIANVS . SOLDANI BENZI NOBILIS . FLOR . FACIEBAT ANNO . 1715
At the left is Ceres seated in a chariot drawn by Triptolemus. On the right are figures bearing agricultural implements. At the left ceutre is a putto with a scroll inscribed: BVRLINGTONVS ERIS/ MANIBVS DATE LILIA PLENIS/PVRPVREOS SPARGANS FLORES. A version of the relief in the Bayerisches Nationalmuseum, Munich (see No. 196 below) is dated 1708, and has on a cartouche on the frame the inscription: FLAVA . CERES . FRONTEM . SPICIS . REDIMITA . JVNCTA . PALATINUM . PAX . BEET . ALMA . SOLVM.
H.M. The Queen

195 AUTUMN. Dark brown patination   Plate 31
h. 47 cm., w. 66 cm.
Signed: MAXIMILIANVS . SOLDANI BENZI NOBILIS . FLORENTINVS . FACIEBAT ANNO . 1715.
On the right are Bacchus and Ariadne. At the left is the drunken Silenus mounted on an ass. A version of the relief in the Bayerisches National-museum, Munich (see No. 196 below) is dated 1708, and has on a cartouche on the frame the inscription: EXUNDENT . VVIS . AVGVSTA . PALATIA . RHENI . PACIFERA . BACCHI . MESSE . TRIUMPHET . AGER.
H.M. The Queen

196 WINTER. Dark brown patination
h. 47 cm., w. 66 cm.
Signed: MAXIMILIANVS . SOLDANI BENZI . NOBILIS . FLORENTINVS . FAC. ANNO 1715. On a shield on the right: VNUM OMNIA CONTRA TELA.

Venus and Mars in the centre visit Vulcan at his forge at the right.
A version of the relief in the Bayerisches National-museum, Munich, is dated 1711, and has on a cartouche on the frame the inscription: PERPOLIAT . LONGIS . VVLCANVS . NOCTIBVS . ARTES . MARS . NVDVS . TACEAT . RIDEAT . ALMA . VENVS.   The terracotta models for all four reliefs are in the Palazzo Pitti, Florence. The four reliefs in Munich were presented by Prince Ferdinando de' Medici (d. 1713) to Kurfürst Johann Wilhelm von der Pfalz, and are illustrated on pl. XIV of *La Galerie Electorale de Dusseldorf* (1778). The present set of reliefs is mentioned by De Champeaux (*Diction-naire des Fondeurs Ciseleurs Modeleurs de Bronze et Doreurs*, I, 1886, pp. 102 f.) as in the Royal collection. According to Lankheit, it was cast in 1715 for Lord Burlington; this is confirmed by the presence of Lord Burlington's arms in the upper right corner of No. 196. A nineteenth-century inventory at Windsor Castle states that the reliefs were presented to King George II by Lord Burleigh [*sic*], and were at one time hung at Kensington Palace. Unsigned replicas of the Summer and Autumn are in the Museum of Fine Arts at the University of Kansas.
Bibl: Tietze-Conrat, in *Jahrbuch der Kunst-historischen Institutes der K.K. Zentralkomission für Deknmalpflege*, XI, 1916, p. 76; Lankheit, in *Münchner Jahrbuch der bildenden Kunst*, VII, 1956, pp. 194–8; Lankheit, in *Register of the Museum of Art in the University of Kansas*, No. 9, 1957, p. 1; Weihrauch, *Bayerisches Nationalmuseum, München: Die Bildwerke in Bronze*, 1956, pp. 172–6.
H.M. The Queen

197 EWER. Dark golden-brown patination. The lid cast separately
h. 79·7 cm.
The function of this and the companion ewer (No. 198) is purely decorative. Both models were reproduced in porcelain at the Doccia factory. It is suggested by Lankheit that a letter of May 31, 1695, addressed by Soldani to Prince Johann Adam von Liechtenstein, which mentions 'due disegni d'Urne richissime' of a braccia and a third in height, relates to the present ewers or to the terracotta models from which they were made.
Bibl: Lankheit, in *Connoisseur*, 1958, November, pp. 159–63.
Victoria and Albert Museum, London

198 EWER. Dark golden-brown patination. The lid cast separately
h. 79·7 cm.
See No. 197.
Victoria and Albert Museum, London

GIOVANNI BATTISTA FOGGINI
(b. Florence 1652–d. Florence 1725)

199 THE FLAYING OF MARSYAS. Rich brown patination
h. 62 cm.   Plate 30
On the base is the inscription DONNE PAR COSME III DE MEDICIS GRAND DUC DE TOSCANE A M. RIGAUD EN 1716. The model is also known through a version in the Bayerisches Nationalmuseum, Munich, which appears to have been presented by the Grand-Duke Cosimo III de' Medici to Kurfürst Johann Wilhelm von der Pfalz. An inferior version is in the Victoria and Albert Museum. The form of the tree in the present bronze differs from that in Munich, in which a syrinx is attached to the branch on the left. When in the possession of the Kurfürst the Munich bronze was accompanied by a companion group of Hercules and Iole, now lost. There is no record of any second version of the Prometheus model (No. 200) which forms a counterpart to the present bronze. The bronzes are dated by Lankheit *c*. 1700.
Coll: Durlacher.
Bibl: Weihrauch, *Bayerisches Nationalmuseum, Munich: Die Bildwerke in Bronze*, 1956, p. 183 (present bronze confused with that in the Victoria and Albert Museum); Lankheit, in *Münchner Jahrbuch der bildenden Kunst*, VII, 1956, pp. 191–2.
Lady Marks, London

200 MERCURY BINDING PROMETHEUS TO THE ROCK. Rich brown patination
h. 43·5 cm.
Companion piece to No. 199 (*q.v.*).
Lady Marks, London

NORTH ITALY

FRANCESCO BERTOS
(Active 1693–1710)

201 HOMAGE TO SCULPTURE. Gilt bronze   Plate 32
h. 75·5 cm.
The group, which is of a quality rarely reached in the bronzes of Bertos, exists in a second larger version without gilding formerly in the possession of Mr Lionel Harris. The two bronzes differ in respect of a number of details; in the Harris version the female figure carried on the shoulder of the centaur is surmounted by a flying putto.
Bibl: Hildburgh, in *Apollo*, XXVII, 1938, pp. 81–5 (for Harris version).
Mr Paul Wallraf, London

202 ALLEGORY OF SCULPTURE. Smooth brown patination
h. 29·5 cm.
The bronze, which is not recorded, is a characteristic work of Bertos.
Mr Brinsley Ford, London

GIUSEPPE MARIA MAZZA
(b. Bologna 1653–d. 1741)

203 VIRGIN AND CHILD
h. 25·1 cm.
No other version of this bronze is known. Attributed to Mazza in the manuscript catalogue of the Auriti collection prepared by Planiscig. It may be compared with Mazza's many terracottas, and with the bronze relief of the Adoration on the Shepherds in S. Clemente, Venice.
H. E. Giacinto Auriti, Rome

INDEX TO ARTISTS

INDEX TO LENDERS

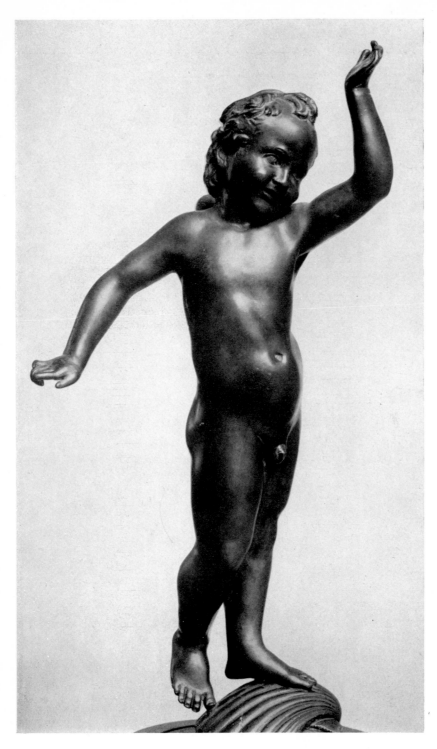

1 Donatello. PUTTO. *Museo Nazionale, Florence* (3)

2 Bertoldo. BATTLE RELIEF (detail). *Museo Nazionale, Florence* (14)

3 Bertoldo. ARION. *Museo Nazionale, Florence* (13)

4 Bertoldo. HERCULES ON HORSEBACK. *Museo Estense, Modena* (15)

5 North Italian, early 16th century. MARSYAS. *Museo Estense, Modena* (36)

6 Pollajuolo. HERCULES AND ANTAEUS. *Museo Nazionale, Florence* (8)

7 Francesco di Giorgio. THE FLAGELLATION. *Galleria Nazionale dell' Umbria, Perugia* (23)

8 Leonardo da Vinci. REARING HORSE. *Mr Pierre Jeannerat, London* (20)

9 Rustici. MERCURY. *Private collection* (21)

10 Antico. MELEAGER. *Victoria and Albert Museum, London* (29)

11 Antico. GONZAGA VASE. *Museo Estense, Modena* (30)

12 Riccio. SATYR AND SATYRESS. *Victoria and Albert Museum, London* (55)

13 Riccio. SEATED SATYR. *Museo Nazionale, Florence* (58)

14 Riccio. SHEPHERD WITH A GOAT. *Museo Nazionale, Florence* (56)

15 Riccio. ABUNDANCE. *Museo Nazionale, Florence* (57)

16 Riccio. WARRIOR ON HORSEBACK. *Victoria and Albert Museum* (48)

17 Riccio. SEATED PAN. *Ashmolean Museum, Oxford* (49)

18 Riccio. ST MARTIN AND THE BEGGAR. *Ca d'Oro, Venice* (45)

19 Sant'Agata. HERCULES. *Ashmolean Museum, Oxford* (83)

20 Atributed to Severo da Ravenna. NEGRO BOY MOUNTED ON A GOAT
The Barber Institute of Fine Arts, Birmingham (73)

21 Venetian, first quarter of the 16th century. HERCULES AND THE SERPENT. *Museo Correr, Venice* (94)

22 Tullio Lombardo. HEAD OF A GIRL. *Museo Estense, Modena* (89A)

23 Sansovino. CHRIST IN LIMBO. *Museo Estense, Modena* (138)

24 Sansovino. JUPITER HOLDING A THUNDERBOLT. *Kunsthistorisches Museum, Vienna* (137)

25 Vittoria. NEPTUNE. *Victoria and Albert Museum, London* (147)

26 Cattaneo. LAZZARO BONAMICO. *Museo Civico, Bassano* (139)

27 Roccatagliata. BACCHUS. *Victoria and Albert Museum, London* (169)

28 Giovanni Bologna. NEPTUNE. *Museo Civico, Bologna* (116)

29 Giovanni Bologna. THE DWARF MORGANTE MOUNTED ON A DRAGON (detail)
Museo Nazionale, Florence (118)

30 Foggini. THE FLAYING OF MARSYAS. *Lady Marks, London* (199)

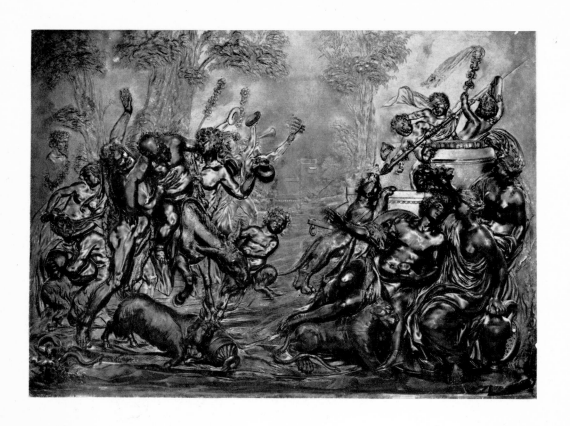

31 Soldani. AUTUMN. *Reproduced by gracious permission of H.M. The Queen* (195)

32 Bertos. HOMAGE TO SCULPTURE. *Mr Paul Wallraf, London* (201)